Houghton Mifflin
Reading

Delights

Senior Authors
J. David Cooper
John J. Pikulski

Authors
David J. Chard
Gilbert Garcia
Claude Goldenberg
Phyllis Hunter
Marjorie Y. Lipson
Shane Templeton
Sheila Valencia
MaryEllen Vogt

Consultants
Linda H. Butler
Linnea C. Ehri
Carla Ford

 HOUGHTON MIFFLIN　　　BOSTON

Cover photography Nick Vedros, Vedros & Associates.

Acknowledgments begin on page 483.

Printed in the U.S.A.

ISBN: 0-618-61937-2

2 3 4 5 6 7 8 9 10 DOW 11 10 09 08 07 06

Delights

Theme 4

Amazing Animals

Theme Wrap-Up
Check Your Progress

BIOGRAPHY

Family Time

Family Time

Theme Wrap-Up

Check Your Progress

Focus on Genre

CHAPTER BOOKS

THE COOL CRAZY CRICKETS

Fiction

Theme 6

Talent Show

8

Theme Wrap-Up

Check Your Progress

Amazing Animals

The Animal Song

Alligator, hedgehog, anteater, bear,
Rattlesnake, buffalo, anaconda, hare.

Mud turtle, whale, glowworm, bat,
Salamander, snail, and Maltese cat.

Polecat, dog, wild otter, rat,
Pelican, hog, dodo, and bat.

Anonymous

Amazing Animals

with Joseph Bruchac

Hello My Friends,

Isn't it fun to watch animals? Sometimes they do things that amaze us. Here's a poem about my dog Toni, who found some new friends in our backyard pond. What's amazing about that? You'll see!

Frog Dog

Our poodle likes
to play with frogs,
she doesn't like to swim.

The frogs leap
right on out to her,
as if to invite her in.

She waits beside
our garden pond
for hours every day.

We shake our heads
and wonder why
those frogs behave that way.

She barks and barks
when they're not there
as if she wants to say,
"Come on you guys,
I'm waiting,
this puppy's here to play."

She never tries
to chase a cat.
She wouldn't dream of biting.
Most poodles
are too dignified
to ever think of fighting.

But frogs, now
that's another thing.
And if my words you doubt,
just come down
to our garden pond
and watch the frogs hop out.

I couldn't believe it when I first saw Toni and the frogs! If you keep your eyes open, you may see animals do amazing things. I'm sure you'll meet some amazing animals in this theme, too. Enjoy!

Animals Can Be Amazing!

Joseph Bruchac thinks that his dog Toni is amazing. What amazing things have you seen an animal do?

You will read about many animals in this theme. As you read, think about what makes each animal amazing. Then you can decide which animal is the most amazing of all!

Internet

To learn about the authors in this theme, visit Education Place. **www.eduplace.com/kids**

Background and Vocabulary

Officer Buckle and Gloria

Genre **Fantasy**

Key Vocabulary

attention

audience

officers

safety

Vocabulary Reader

Training a **Police Dog**

e • Glossary

16

Safety Officers

Police **officers** who visit schools to talk about **safety** are sometimes called safety officers. In the story you're going to read next, an officer and his partner give safety speeches at an elementary school. Like the **audience** in this story, you should always pay close **attention** to a safety officer's speech. He or she will explain many ways to avoid accidents and to stay safe.

Bicycle and In-line Skating Safety

1. Always wear a helmet.

2. Obey traffic signals.

3.

FACT FILE

- Peggy Rathmann was born in St. Paul, Minnesota.
- The first time she tried to write a children's book, the book was 150 pages long!
- *Officer Buckle and Gloria* won the Caldecott Medal in 1996.
- Officer Buckle's safety tips are ideas Ms. Rathmann collected from her nieces, nephew, and other children. She gave them each twenty-five dollars for any safety tip she used in the book.

Meet the Author and Illustrator

Peggy Rathmann

Other books by Peggy Rathmann:
Ruby the Copycat
Good Night, Gorilla

Internet

To find out how Peggy Rathmann's dog is a lot like Gloria, take a look at Education Place.

www.eduplace.com/kids

OFFICER BUCKLE AND GLORIA

PEGGY RATHMANN

Strategy Focus

Officer Buckle's safety speeches are more exciting than he'd planned. As you read the story, **monitor** how well you understand what happens in it.

Officer Buckle knew more safety tips than anyone else in Napville.

Every time he thought of a new one, he thumbtacked it to his bulletin board.

Safety Tip #77

NEVER stand on a SWIVEL CHAIR.

Officer Buckle shared his safety tips
with the students at Napville School.
Nobody ever listened.
Sometimes, there was snoring.

22

Afterward, it was business as usual.

Mrs. Toppel, the principal, took down the welcome banner.

"NEVER stand on a SWIVEL CHAIR," said Officer Buckle, but Mrs. Toppel didn't hear him.

Then one day, Napville's police department
bought a police dog named Gloria.

When it was time for Officer Buckle to give
the safety speech at the school, Gloria went along.

24

"Children, this is Gloria," announced Officer
Buckle. "Gloria obeys my commands. Gloria, SIT!"
And Gloria sat.

Officer Buckle gave Safety Tip Number One:
"KEEP your SHOELACES tied!"
The children sat up and stared.

Officer Buckle checked to see if Gloria was
sitting at attention. She was.

"Safety Tip Number Two," said Officer Buckle.

"ALWAYS wipe up spills BEFORE someone SLIPS AND FALLS!"

The children's eyes popped.

Officer Buckle checked on Gloria again.

"Good dog," he said.

Officer Buckle thought of a safety tip he had discovered that morning.

"NEVER leave a THUMBTACK where you might SIT on it!"
The audience roared.

Officer Buckle grinned. He said the rest of the tips with *plenty* of expression.

The children clapped their hands and cheered. Some of them laughed until they cried.

Officer Buckle was surprised. He had never noticed how funny safety tips could be.

After *this* safety speech, there wasn't a single accident.

The next day, an enormous envelope arrived
at the police station. It was stuffed with thank-you
letters from the students at Napville School.

Every letter had a drawing of Gloria on it.

Officer Buckle thought the drawings showed a lot of imagination.

His favorite letter was written on a star-shaped piece of paper. It said:

You and Gloria make a good team.

Your friend,
Claire

P.S. I always wear a crash helmet. (Safety Tip #7)

Officer Buckle was thumbtacking Claire's letter to his bulletin board when the phones started ringing. Grade schools, high schools, and day-care centers were calling about the safety speech.

"Officer Buckle," they said, "our students want to hear your safety tips! And please, bring along that police dog."

Officer Buckle told his safety tips to 313 schools.
Everywhere he and Gloria went, children sat up
and listened.

After every speech, Officer Buckle took Gloria
out for ice cream.

Officer Buckle loved having a buddy.

Then one day, a television news team videotaped
Officer Buckle in the state-college auditorium.

When he finished Safety Tip Number Ninety-nine,
DO NOT GO SWIMMING DURING ELECTRICAL
STORMS!, the students jumped to their feet and
applauded.

That night, Officer Buckle watched himself
on the 10 o'clock news.

43

The next day, the principal of Napville School telephoned the police station.

"Good morning, Officer Buckle! It's time for our safety speech!"

Officer Buckle frowned.

"I'm not giving any more speeches! Nobody looks at me, anyway!"

"Oh," said Mrs. Toppel. "Well! How about Gloria? Could she come?"

Someone else from the police station gave Gloria a ride to the school.

Gloria sat onstage looking lonely. Then she fell asleep. So did the audience.

After Gloria left, Napville School had its biggest accident ever. . . .

It started with a puddle of banana pudding . . .

SPLAT! SPLATTER!

SPLOOSH!

Everyone slid smack into Mrs. Toppel, who
screamed and let go of her hammer.

47

The next morning, a pile of letters arrived at the police station.

Every letter had a drawing of the accident.

Officer Buckle was shocked.

At the bottom of the pile was a note written on a paper star.

Officer Buckle smiled.

The note said:

Gloria missed you yesterday!

Your friend,
Claire

P.S. Don't worry, I was wearing my helmet! (Safety Tip #7)

Gloria gave Officer Buckle a big kiss on the nose.

Officer Buckle gave Gloria a nice pat on the back.

Then, Officer Buckle thought of his best safety tip yet. . . .

Safety Tip #101

"ALWAYS STICK WITH YOUR BUDDY!"

Think About the Selection

1. Choose two safety tips from the story. Explain why they are important.

2. How do Peggy Rathmann's illustrations make this story funny?

3. How do you think Officer Buckle felt when he saw himself on the 10 o'clock news?

4. What does this story teach about teamwork and friendship?

5. **Connecting/Comparing** In what ways is Gloria an amazing animal?

Expressing

Write a Thank-You Letter

The students at Napville School sent letters to Officer Buckle and Gloria. Write your own thank-you letter. Tell Officer Buckle and Gloria what you thought of their speeches. Tell what you learned about safety.

> **Tips**
>
> - To get started, look at the letters in the story.
> - Be sure to include the date, greeting, closing, and your name.

Make a School Safety Poster

Identify places in your school where safety tips would help. Make a poster showing one of these tips. Be sure to explain why students should follow it.

Present a Safety Tip

Work with a partner. Think of a safety tip that your class should follow. Have one partner act out the safety tip while the other explains it. Can you make your presentation as exciting as Officer Buckle and Gloria's?

Tips

- **Brainstorm a list of possible safety tips.**
- **Look at the class as you present your safety tip.**

Internet

Complete a Web Crossword Puzzle

What started with a puddle of banana pudding? Test what you've learned from the story by completing the crossword puzzle on Education Place.

www.eduplace.com/kids

Genre

Maps

Skill: How to Read a Map

- Look for a **key**, or **legend**, that shows what the symbols or colors on the map mean.

- Use the **compass rose** to find the directions of north, south, east, and west.

- Read the **labels** to find cities, states, countries, or other places the map shows.

The Story of Owney

from *Postal Pack for Elementary School Students*, National Postal Museum and Smithsonian Institution

More than one hundred years ago, a little dog wandered into a post office and made himself at home among the mailbags. He loved traveling with the mail. Once, when a mailbag accidentally fell off a cart, Owney stayed with the bag to protect it until the postal clerks came back to fetch it.

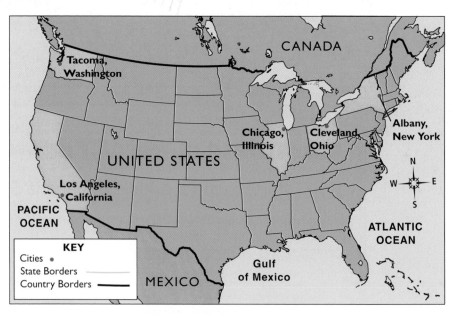

These are just some of the cities Owney visited.

Owney became a famous dog. He jumped onto mail trains whenever he liked. The clerks loved having him along because he was a good luck charm. There was never a railroad accident when Owney was aboard. Wherever he went, postal clerks made a dog tag for him, so others would know where he had traveled. The National Postal Museum has more than one thousand Owney tags that show all the places Owney visited.

Owney loved to ride in the mail cars.

A Research Report

A research report tells facts about a topic in the writer's own words. Use this student's writing as a model when you write a research report of your own.

The Harp Seal

My favorite animal is the harp seal. I've found out a lot about the harp seal that I would like to share with you.

A real harp seal has beautiful gray fur and lives in the cold water in the North Atlantic Ocean. Harp seals are happiest when they are in the water. Their flippers really help them swim quickly. When harp seals are on the icy land, they have to wiggle their bodies so they can move. Their front flippers have claws that help them hold on to the ice and rocks. Mostly they just stay in the water.

When harp seals are in the water they eat shrimp and squid. They also eat big fish. The seals have to be very careful in the water. That's when the polar bears, sharks, and killer whales could swim up and hurt them. Another interesting thing about harp seals is that they don't have ears! They hear sounds through their heads, instead.

The harp seal is very cute, even though it's pretty big. It grows to be six feet long. Someday I would like to see one in person.

A good **ending** wraps up the report.

Meet the Author

Celsey B.

Grade: two
State: Georgia
Hobbies: horseback riding, swimming, and skating
What she'd like to be when she grows up: a horseback rider who jumps or a dentist

Rebecca Stefoff
ANT

LIVING THINGS

Ant

Genre **Nonfiction**

Key Vocabulary

antennae

cocoons

colonies

fungus

larvae

tunnels

Vocabulary Reader

The Leafcutter Ant

e Glossary

58

Fun Facts About Ants

Have you ever looked closely at an ant? In the next selection, you'll learn some fun facts about ants from all around the world.

Ants usually live under the ground in groups called **colonies**. Colonies of ants build **tunnels** and store food.

Ants guide themselves inside their tunnels by using the two long **antennae** on their heads.

Some ants grow their own food. They eat a special **fungus**, or mold, that they make from leaves.

Young ants, or **larvae**, hatch from **cocoons**.

Meet the Author
Rebecca Stefoff

Other books by Rebecca Stefoff:
Octopus
Owl
Butterfly

Rebecca Stefoff's favorite things to do are traveling and watching animals. She enjoys birdwatching and has traveled all over the world. She has gone scuba diving to observe moray eels, barracuda, and brightly colored coral fish.

When at home in Oregon, she watches the crabs, seals, and shore birds that live nearby.

Ms. Stefoff thinks ants are interesting to watch because they live almost everywhere. "Wherever you go, they're there," she says.

Internet

Did you know that one of Rebecca Stefoff's favorite animals is the slug? Find out more about this author by visiting Education Place.

www.eduplace.com/kids

Rebecca Stefoff

ANT

As you read this nonfiction selection, think of **questions** to ask your classmates about the amazing world of ants.

61

black ant, Costa Rica

Ants.

They're everywhere. You can see ants in almost any part of the world.

But you hardly ever see just one ant. If you see an ant, you will probably find lots of other ants nearby.

anthill, Australia

Ants live and work together in busy, crowded groups called colonies. Most colonies are in tunnels under the ground. The ants carry dirt out of the tunnels to make a pile. We call these piles anthills.

anthill in sidewalk

When you see an anthill in a sidewalk crack, you know there is a city of ants under the sidewalk.

64

Some anthills are huge and filled with tunnels.
An ant colony has lived under this tree for years.
Each year the ants dig new tunnels and make the
anthill a little bigger.

anthill, East Africa

Every ant has two long, waving stalks on its head. These are its antennae. They are like a nose and fingers all in one.

The antennae tell the ant what is going on around it. They help it find food and then find its way back to its colony.

These two ants are "talking" by rubbing their antennae together. The big ant is the queen. She is the mother of all the ants in the colony. The little ant is a worker. Workers take care of the queen's eggs and bring food to the colony.

red ants transferring food

Ants do all kinds of things together. They pass pieces of food to one another. Sometimes they even carry each other around.

Some jobs are too big for one ant. That's when ants team up. A bunch of little ants working together can carry a big dead bug. It will make a fine meal for the colony.

ants carrying dead stick insect, Brazil

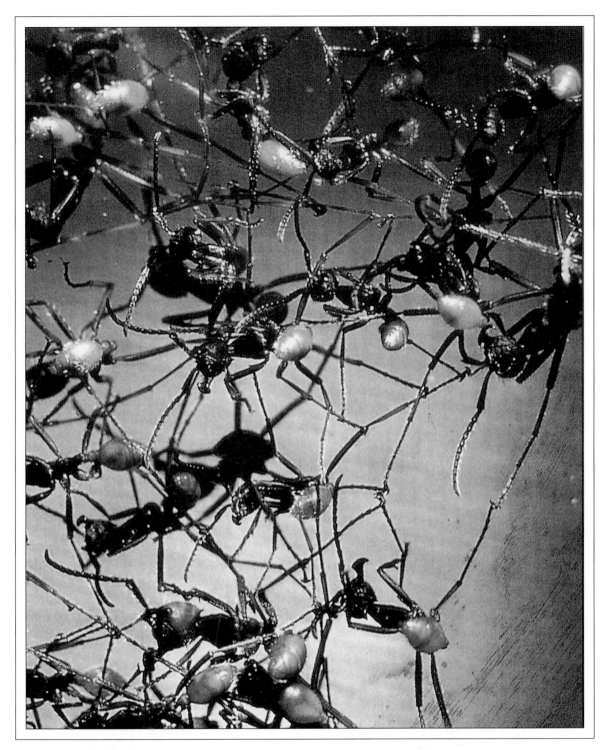

ant bridge, Panama

Ants take a shortcut between tree branches. Some of them hold one another's legs to make a bridge. Others can walk across the bridge to the new branch.

Carpenter ants live in wood. A pile of yellow sawdust on a log means that carpenter ants are busy inside, chewing new tunnels.

Deep in the log, the queen's eggs are turning into larvae. When the larvae hatch from their cocoons, they look like little worms. Later the larvae will turn into ants and pour out of the log.

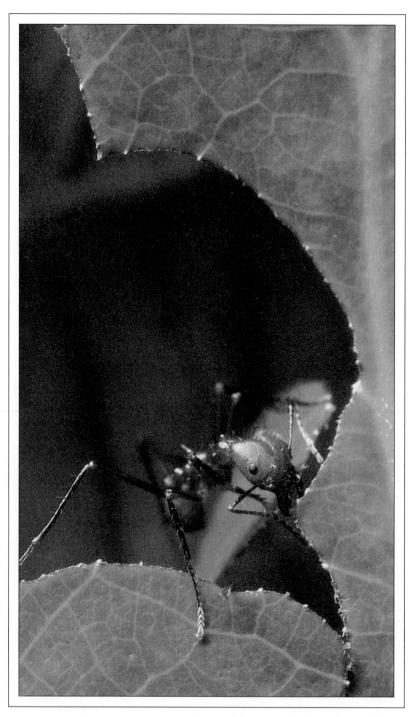

leafcutter ants, Costa Rica

Leafcutter ants live in Central and South America. Some people call them parasol ants. Do you know why?

The ants chew off pieces of leaves and carry them back to their tunnels. They march with the leaves held over their heads like little sunshades, or parasols.

The ants don't eat the leaves. They chew them into a paste. A yellow fungus grows on the paste, and the ants eat the fungus.

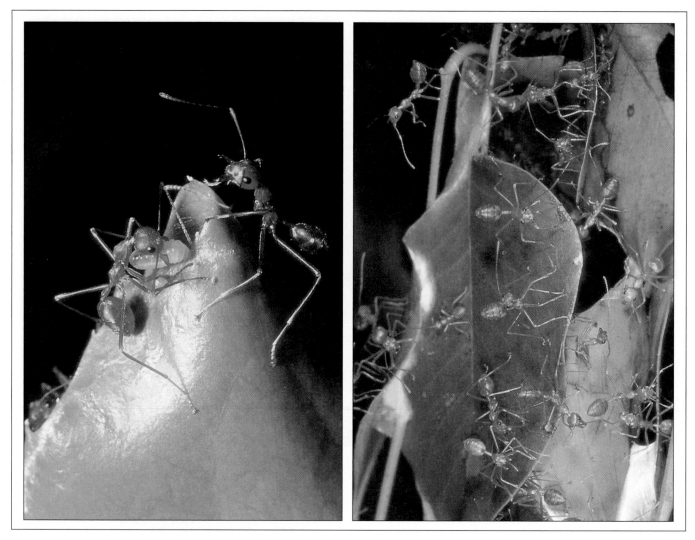

weaver ants with larva   *white larval thread binds leaves*

Weaver ants live in trees in southern Asia and on Pacific islands. They make nests by fastening leaves together with sticky silk thread. The thread comes from the young ants, or larvae. Older ants hold the larvae that spin the thread.

  Teams of ants join together into chains to bend the big, stiff leaves.

nest making, Australia

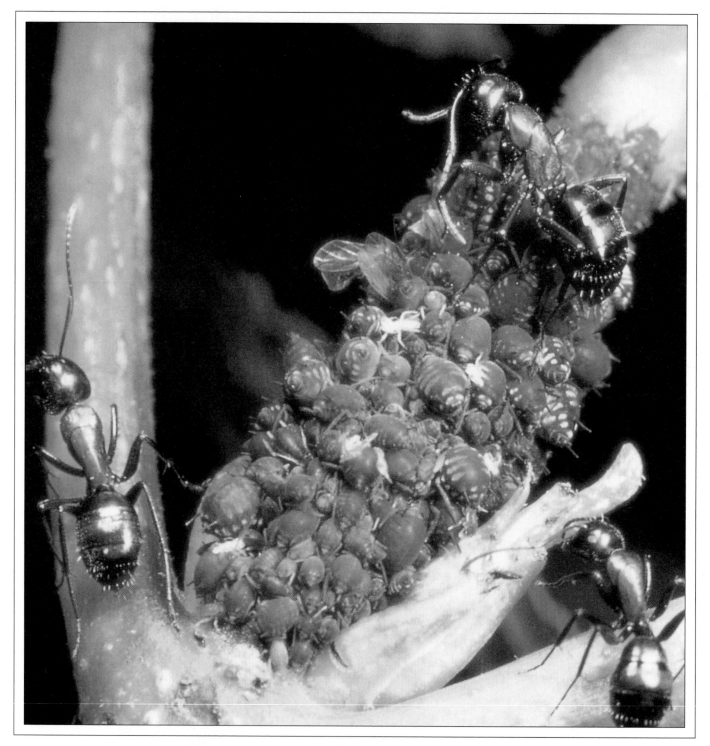

farmer ants with aphids, New York

ants "milking" caterpillar

Some ants eat juices that come from inside other insects. They take care of these insects and "milk" them for their juice, like a farmer milks a herd of cows.

The little green bugs are plant eaters called aphids. The ants tending them are called farmer ants.

A rmy ants live in tropical jungles. They march from place to place, eating plants and insects as they go. They climb right over logs and rocks and even houses.

A colony of army ants on the march covers the ground like a moving, munching carpet. Some colonies are as wide as a street and as long as a city block.

army ants, Costa Rica

A lot of little ants working together can beat one big black beetle. When it comes to teamwork, ants are experts.

Can you pick up your mother and carry her over your head? You could if you were an ant. Ants are very strong. They can carry things that weigh a lot more than they do. It takes only two ants to lift this fat caterpillar.

Ants live in colonies that
are like cities. They help one
another, and they work together
on big jobs.

I think ants are a lot like us.
Do you?

Think About the Selection

1. Which facts about ants did you find most amazing?

2. Find three questions the author asks the reader. Why does she ask questions instead of just telling facts?

3. How are ant colonies like cities? Give examples from the selection.

4. In what ways do ants work in teams?

5. **Connecting/Comparing** *Ant* is a nonfiction selection. *Officer Buckle and Gloria* is fiction. Compare the two.

Informing

Write a Report

Choose a type of ant described in the selection. In your own words, write a report that tells facts about the ant that you chose.

Tips

- Use complete sentences.
- Your report should be one or two paragraphs long.

Count Legs

Ants have six legs. If there are five ants on a leaf, how many legs are there in all? Use numbers from the problem to write a multiplication sentence.

Bonus If three more ants climb onto the leaf, how many legs are there in all?

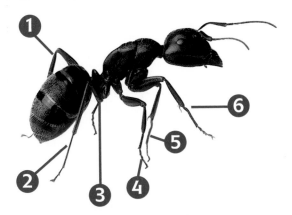

Make Ant Prints

Here's a fun way to decorate a card or plain book cover. Press the eraser end of a pencil into black paint. Print ant bodies on paper. Then draw in the details with a fine-tip black pen. If you want to make red ants, use red paint!

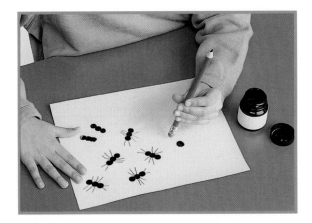

Internet

Solve a Web Maze

Help an ant find its way through a Web maze and back to its colony. Print a maze from Education Place, and then fill it in.

www.eduplace.com/kids

Genre

Song Lyrics

Skill: How to Read Song Lyrics

1. Skim the **lyrics**, or words of the song, before singing.

2. Sing the first **verse** and then the **chorus**.

3. Repeat for the remaining verses.

The Ants Go Marching
Traditional Children's Song

1. The ants go march-ing one by one, Hur-rah,— Hur-rah.— The ants go march-ing one by one, Hur-rah,— Hur-rah.— The ants go march-ing one by one; The lit-tle one stops to have some fun, and they all go march-ing down in-to the ground to get out of the rain. Boom! Boom! Boom!

2. The ants go marching two by two,
    Hurrah, Hurrah. *(repeat)*
The ants go marching two by two;
    The little one stops to tie his shoe.

Chorus:
And they all go marching down into the ground
to get out of the rain. Boom! Boom! Boom!

3. The ants go marching three by three;
    Hurrah, Hurrah. *(repeat)*
The ants go marching three by three;
    The little one stops to climb a tree.
Chorus

4. The ants go marching four by four;
    Hurrah, Hurrah. *(repeat)*
The ants go marching four by four;
    The little one stops to shut the door.
Chorus

5. The ants go marching five by five;
    Hurrah, Hurrah. *(repeat)*
The ants go marching five by five;
    The little one stops to take a dive.
Chorus

Background and Vocabulary

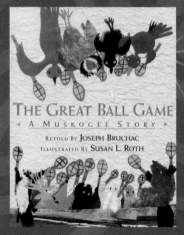

The Great Ball Game

Genre Folktale

Key Vocabulary

accept
advantage
arguments
penalty
quarrel

Vocabulary Reader

A BIG Tennis Match
by James Allen

e • Glossary

Ball Games

In the story you are about to read, two groups agree to play a ball game in order to end a **quarrel**. Each group believes it has an **advantage** over the other one. Both groups agree that the winners may set a **penalty** that the losers must **accept**.

Ball games have been played in the Americas for hundreds of years.

Native Americans sometimes played these games as a way of settling **arguments**.

One game, which we now call lacrosse, was played with a deerskin ball and long poles that were used to toss the ball.

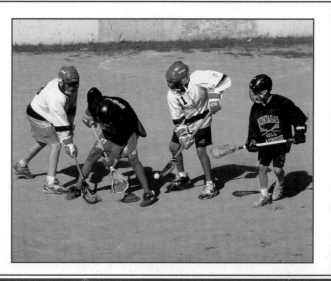

Meet the Author
Joseph Bruchac

Joseph Bruchac's grandfather, a member of the Abenaki tribe, told him many traditional folk stories. Mr. Bruchac enjoys telling the stories that his grandfather passed on to him, as well as folktales from other Native American tribes.

Meet the Illustrator
Susan L. Roth

Susan L. Roth used cut paper collected from all over the world to make the illustrations for this book: red umbrella paper from Thailand, an envelope from Tibet, blue paper from Japan, and green paper from Italy.

Internet

To learn more about Joseph Bruchac and Susan L. Roth, visit Education Place.

www.eduplace.com/kids

90

THE GREAT BALL GAME
◄ A MUSKOGEE STORY ►

RETOLD BY **JOSEPH BRUCHAC**

ILLUSTRATED BY **SUSAN L. ROTH**

Strategy Focus

Who will win the great ball game? As you read, stop and **summarize** the important parts of the story.

Long ago the Birds and Animals had a great argument.

"We who have wings are better than you," said the Birds.

"That is not so," the Animals replied. "We who have teeth are better."

The two sides argued back and forth. Their quarrel went on and on, until it seemed they would go to war because of it.

Then Crane, the leader of the Birds, and Bear,
the leader of the Animals, had an idea.
"Let us have a ball game," Crane said. "The
first side to score a goal will win the argument."

"This idea is good," said Bear. "The side that loses will have to accept the penalty given by the other side."

So they walked and flew to a field, and there they divided up into two teams.

On one side went all those who had wings. They were the Birds.

On the other side went those with teeth. They were the Animals.

But when the teams were formed, one creature
was left out: Bat. He had wings *and* teeth! He flew
back and forth between the two sides.

First he went to the Animals. "I have teeth," he
said. "I must be on your side."

But Bear shook his head. "It would not be fair,"
he said. "You have wings. You must be a Bird."

So Bat flew to the other side. "Take me," he
said to the Birds, "for you see I have wings."
     But the Birds laughed at him. "You are too little
to help us. We don't want you," they jeered.

Then Bat went back to the Animals. "Please let me join your team," he begged them. "The Birds laughed at me and would not accept me."

So Bear took pity on the little bat. "You are not very big," said Bear, "but sometimes even the small ones can help. We will accept you as an Animal, but you must hold back and let the bigger Animals play first."

Two poles were set up as the goalposts at each
end of the field. Then the game began.

Each team played hard. On the Animals' side
Fox and Deer were swift runners, and Bear cleared
the way for them as they played. Crane and Hawk,
though, were even swifter, and they stole the ball
each time before the Animals could reach their goal.

100

Soon it became clear that the Birds had the advantage. Whenever they got the ball, they would fly up into the air and the Animals could not reach them. The Animals guarded their goal well, but they grew tired as the sun began to set.

Just as the sun sank below the horizon, Crane took the ball and flew toward the poles. Bear tried to stop him, but stumbled in the dim light and fell. It seemed as if the Birds would surely win.

Suddenly a small dark shape flew onto the field and stole the ball from Crane just as he was about to reach the poles. It was Bat. He darted from side to side across the field, for he did not need light to find his way. None of the Birds could catch him or block him.

105

Holding the ball, Bat flew right between the
poles at the other end! The Animals had won!

This is how Bat came to be accepted as an Animal. He was allowed to set the penalty for the Birds.

"You Birds," Bat said, "must leave this land for half of each year."

So it is that the Birds fly south each winter...

And every day at dusk Bat still comes flying to
see if the Animals need him to play ball.

Think About the Selection

1. What event in nature does this tale explain?

2. How might the story have been different if Bat had not played the game?

3. If Bat had helped the Birds win, what sort of penalty might he have set for the Animals?

4. Do you think the story shows a good way to settle an argument? Why or why not?

5. **Connecting/Comparing** All of the animals in this theme work in teams. Describe each type of team, and then compare two or more teams.

Expressing

Writing a Folktale

Bears go to sleep for the winter. Spiders make webs. Moths fly toward lights. Think of an animal. Write a folktale that explains why the animal acts the way it does.

Tips

- Observe a pet or other animal to get ideas.
- Use a story map to organize your ideas.

Make a Fact File

List what you've learned about bats from reading this selection. Then look for information about bats in an encyclopedia or science book. Make a bat fact file using the information you've collected.

Create Game Rules

The Birds and Animals played a game without any written rules. Write a set of rules for them to follow when playing their game. Explain how rules can help them play together fairly.

Take a Web Field Trip

Learn more about amazing animals. Visit Education Place to discover interesting facts about all kinds of animals.

www.eduplace.com/kids

Bat Attitude

from 3–2–1 Contact
by Lynn O'Donnell

Veronica Thomas has been crazy about bats ever since she could walk. Her room is littered with bat puppets, bat key chains, bat books, and glow-in-the-dark bat T-shirts.

Veronica's obsession with bats might have something to do with her dad's job. He's the curator of mammals at the Wildlife Conservation Society (Bronx Zoo) in New York City. Veronica saw her first bat there when she was just a year old.

Batgirl Forever

You might think Veronica wants to be a bat expert when she grows up. But her dream is to become a paleontologist. Paleontologists are scientists who study animal fossils. "Who knows?" says Veronica. "Maybe someday I'll find a fossil of a bat."

Little Brown Bat

The little brown bat of North America is a big eater. In one hour, it can catch and gulp down 600 mosquitoes.

Veronica's Favorite Bat

Straw-colored Flying Fox

Bats on the Brain

Veronica and her dad built a bat house in their backyard. Bat houses give bats a safe place to live and raise a family. Veronica checks it every day for signs of the winged critters.

113

Snout

Ear

Fingers

Foot

Bat Anatomy

Although bats fly, they're not birds
— they are mammals.

Make an Origami Bat

What you need:
Black or brown construction paper, googly-eyes (optional)

What you do:
First cut paper so that it is a perfect square,
equal on all sides.

Then follow the illustrated steps.

Thumb

Wing membrane

Dinner Call

Bats send out high-pitched sounds. When the sound bounces back off an object, bats can tell if there's food nearby. Some moths send beeps to a bat to trick it. The bat thinks it's found another bat — and the moth doesn't become bat food.

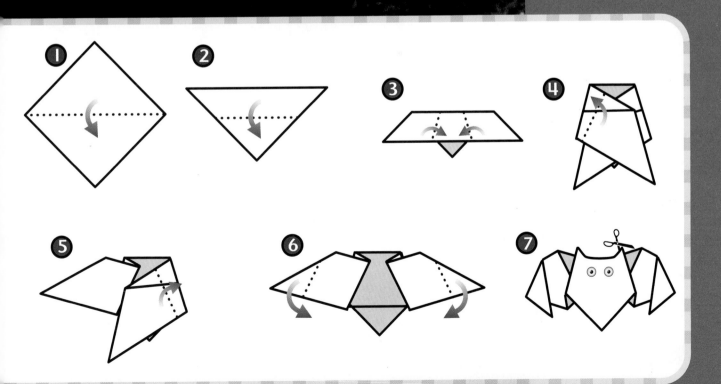

Check Your Progress

What made the animals in this theme amazing to you? Get ready to read and compare two more selections about amazing animals. Then practice some test–taking skills.

On pages 12–14, Joseph Bruchac describes how much fun it is to watch animals. What would you tell him about the animals in this theme?

Think about what makes the animals amazing in the next two selections. How do they compare with the other amazing animals in this theme?

Read and Compare

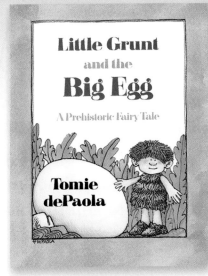

Find out what happens when a boy finds the biggest egg he has ever seen.

Try these strategies:
Predict and Infer
Summarize

Fantasy

Discover facts about dinosaurs that lived on earth millions of years ago.

Try these strategies:
Monitor and Clarify
Question

Nonfiction

Strategies in Action *Be sure to use all your reading strategies as you read these selections.*

Little Grunt and the Big Egg

written and illustrated by Tomie dePaola

Little Grunt and his family live in a mountain cave. One day Little Grunt brings home the biggest egg he has ever seen. The whole family is surprised when the egg hatches into a baby dinosaur. The Grunts agree to let Little Grunt keep the dinosaur as a pet.

"I'm going to call him George," said Little Grunt. Little Grunt and George became great pals.

But there was a problem. The cave stayed the same size, but George didn't. He began to grow.

And GROW.

And GROW.

The cave got very crowded.

And there were other problems.

George wasn't housebroken.

George ate ALL the leaves off ALL the trees and ALL the bushes ALL around the cave. But still he was hungry.

George liked to play — rough. George stepped on things.

And when he sneezed — well, it was a disaster.

"Ooga, ooga! Enough is enough!" said the Grunts.

"Either that dinosaur goes, or I go," said Unca Grunt.

"I spend all day getting food for him," said Ant Grunt.

"Achoo!" said Papa Grunt. "I told you I was allergic to him."

"He stepped on all my cooking pots and broke them," said Mama Grunt.

"I guess it wasn't a good idea to keep him," said
Granny Grunt. "How about a nice *little* cockroach.
They make nice pets."

"I'm in charge here," said Chief Rockhead Grunt.
"And I say, *That giant lizard goes!*"

"Ooga, ooga! Yes! Yes!" said all the Grunts.

"But you promised," said Little Grunt.

The next morning, Little Grunt took George away from the cave, out to where he had found him in the first place.

"Good-bye, George," said Little Grunt. "I'll sure miss you."

"Waaargh," said George.

Big tears rolled down both their cheeks. Sadly, Little Grunt watched as George walked slowly into the swamp.

"I'll never see him again," sobbed Little Grunt.

The days and months went by, and Little Grunt still missed George. He dreamed about him at night and drew pictures of him by day.

"Little Grunt certainly misses that dinosaur," said Mama Grunt.

"He'll get over it," said Papa Grunt.

"It's nice and peaceful here again," said Ant and Unca Grunt.

"I still say a cockroach makes a nice pet," said Granny Grunt.

"Ooga, ooga. Torches out. Everyone in bed," said Chief Rockhead.

That night, the cave started to shake. The floor
began to pitch, and loud rumblings filled the air.

"Earthquake!" cried the Grunts, and they rushed to
the opening of the cave.

"No, it's not," said Granny Grunt. "Look! Volcano!"

And sure enough, the big volcano was erupting all
over the place. Steam and rocks and black smoke shot
out of the top. Around the cave, big rocks and boulders
tumbled and bounced.

"We're trapped! We're trapped!" shouted the Grunts. "What are we going to do?"

"Don't ask me!" said Chief Rockhead. "I resign."

"Now we have no leader," cried Ant Grunt.

"Now we're really in trouble!" shouted Papa Grunt.

The lava was pouring out of the volcano in a wide, flaming river and was heading straight for the cave.

There wasn't enough time for the Grunts to escape. All of a sudden, the Grunts heard a different noise. "Waaargh! Wonk!"

"It's George," cried Little Grunt. "He's come to save us."

"Ooga, ooga! Quick!" said the Grunts as they all jumped on George's long neck and long back and long tail.

And before you could say Tyrannosaurus rex, George carried them far away to safety.

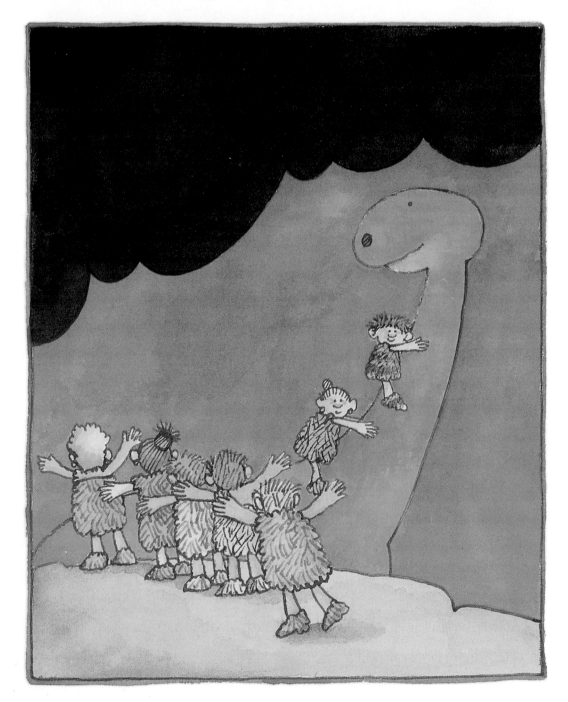

Mighty Dinosaurs

by Judith Simpson

The Age of Dinosaurs

Dinosaurs roamed the Earth millions of years ago. Dinosaur means "terrible lizard" and, like lizards, dinosaurs were reptiles. We know a lot about dinosaurs from their remains, which we have found buried in rocks and beneath sand. Dinosaurs had knobby or pebbly skin and laid eggs. Some walked on two legs, others moved on all four. Dinosaurs fed on different things — some ate only plants, others ate meat and hunted for their food.

Dinosaurs came in different shapes and sizes. Some had very large bodies and tiny heads. Some dinosaurs had spikes or bumps on their backs. Others had horns or crests on their heads. Their skin was thick and rough. People did not live on Earth until long after dinosaurs died out.

Meat Eaters

Meat-eating dinosaurs had good eyesight and a strong sense of smell. They had much larger brains than plant-eating dinosaurs, so they could plan attacks to catch their prey. Some meat eaters lived on eggs, insects, lizards, small furry animals, and fish. Others gathered in packs to kill dinosaurs that were much bigger than themselves. *Tyrannosaurus* could be three times as tall as a man and was one of the largest meat-eating dinosaurs.

◀ ***Tyrannosaurus*** **was one of the last dinosaurs on Earth.**

Plant Eaters

Not all dinosaurs were fierce hunters. Some ate only plants. For most of the age of dinosaurs, the weather was warm and wet. Plants grew easily and there were lots to choose from. Plant-eating dinosaurs needed large amounts of food to give them energy. Some roamed the land grazing on low-growing ferns. Others had long necks and, like giraffes, could stretch up to reach leaves from the tops of the tallest trees.

▶ *Apatosaurus* **was an eating machine. To stay alive, it had to chomp through plants all day long.**

Skeletons and Skulls

Dinosaurs' bones, teeth, and claws have been in the ground for so long that they have turned to stone and become fossils. Many are in broken pieces. Scientists can put fossils together to show what a dinosaur looked like when it was alive. Fossil bones tell us how a dinosaur moved. Fossil claws tell us how it hunted. Fossil teeth tell us what it ate. Space inside the skull tells us the size of its brain.

Dinosaurs disappeared about 65 million years ago. What killed them? Nobody knows for sure.

◀ *Allosaurus* had hinged jaws. It could swallow large pieces of meat in one gulp.

▶ When dinosaurs' teeth wore out, they grew new ones.

Think and Compare

1. Compare *Little Grunt and the Big Egg* with *Mighty Dinosaurs*. Tell some things that George does that real dinosaurs could not do.

2. What safety tips could Officer Buckle and Gloria give to Little Grunt?

3. Which animal in this theme would you like to learn more about? Why?

4. In this theme, which characters show how important it is to work together? Give reasons for your answers.

Strategies in Action Tell about one or two places in *Mighty Dinosaurs* where you used reading strategies.

Write a Journal Entry

Write a journal entry from the point of view of an ant that lived during the dinosaur age. Tell what happened one day when the ant looked up and saw a dinosaur!

Tips
- Describe what the ant sees, hears, and feels.
- Use details about ants and dinosaurs from the stories in this theme.

Vocabulary Items

Some test items ask you to decide the meaning of a word in a sentence. A test for *Little Grunt and the Big Egg* might have this test item.

> **Fill in the circle next to the best answer for the test item below.**
>
> 1 Read this sentence from *Little Grunt and the Big Egg*. "Around the cave, big rocks and boulders tumbled and bounced." What does **tumbled** mean?
>
> ○ rested quietly   ○ jumped up
>
> ● fell down   ○ stayed still

① Understand the question.

Find the word that the question is asking about. Decide what you need to do.

The question asks what **tumbled** means. I need to look at the choices and choose the best meaning of that word.

2 **Think about what the word means.**

Think about the parts of the word. Think about how the word is used.

> I know that what the boulders did happened in the past because **tumbled** ends with **-ed**. I can tell from the sentence that the boulders were moving.

 3 **Narrow the choices. Then choose the best answer.**

Try each answer choice in the sentence. Which choices are wrong? Have a good reason for choosing an answer.

> The boulders moved, so **rested quietly** and **stayed still** are not right. **Jumped up** is not right, because boulders cannot do that. I choose **fell down**.

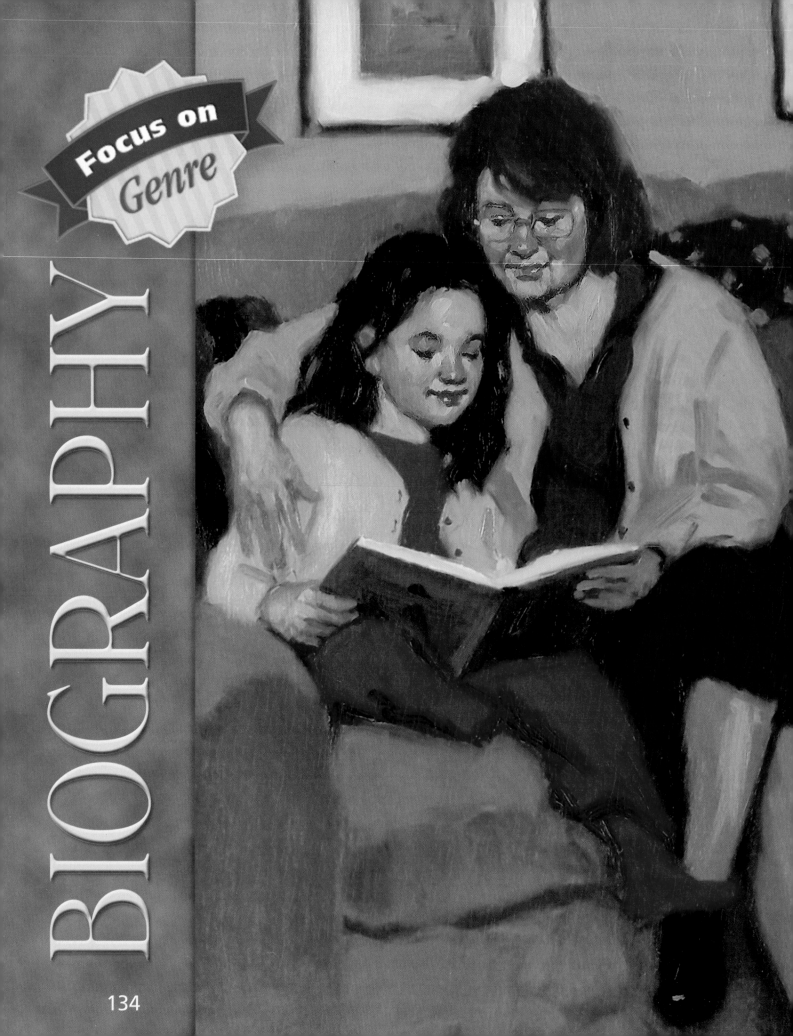

BIOGRAPHY

134

Biography

Is there someone you've always wanted to meet? Read that person's **biography**!

A biography is a true story about a person's life. It gives **facts** about what the person did. It tells about **events** that happened to the person. Meet some special people in these short biographies.

CONTENTS

REACH FOR THE STARS

The Ellen Ochoa Story

BY ELENA ALONSO

It was April 17, 1993. The space shuttle *Discovery* was about to return to Earth after more than nine days in space. One of the five astronauts on board, Dr. Ellen Ochoa, had just made history. Dr. Ochoa had become the first Hispanic woman to travel in space.

Discovery lifts off.

Ellen Ochoa was born in 1958 in Los Angeles, California. She was eleven years old when astronauts walked on the moon for the first time. She didn't dream then that some day she too would become an astronaut.

The crew of
Discovery, 1993

"At that time, there weren't any women astronauts and also very few who were scientists," she says. "So it didn't occur to me when I was in school that this was something I could grow up and do."

Today, Ellen enjoys speaking to children about her work as an astronaut. She encourages children, especially girls, to study math and science.

Ellen's favorite subjects in school were math and music. She also played the flute. In fact, she became so good at it that she was asked to play with a youth orchestra in San Diego.

The space shuttle's
cargo bay

"Only you put limitations on yourself about what you can achieve, so don't be afraid to reach for the stars."

Several years after college, Ellen decided that she really wanted to learn how to be an astronaut. She moved to Houston, Texas, where the NASA space program is located. Meanwhile, she took up a new hobby: she learned how to fly an airplane!

In 1990, NASA picked Ellen for its astronaut program. Three years later, she made her first space shuttle flight. Her job was to work a robotic arm that can send small satellites into space and then catch them again.

Ellen Ochoa with her son

Ellen Ochoa flew with six other astronauts on the *Discovery* in 1999.

Since her first flight, Ellen has spent almost 500 hours in space. On one trip, Ellen and her team traveled 4 million miles in 235 hours and 13 minutes!

Ellen is proud to be the first Hispanic female astronaut. She tells children to work hard to become whatever they want to be. She says, "Only you put limitations on yourself about what you can achieve, so don't be afraid to reach for the stars."

PRESIDENT
Theodore Roosevelt

by Stephen Berman

BEING PRESIDENT OF THE UNITED STATES is something that many people only dream about. But Theodore Roosevelt did more than dream about it. "Keep your eyes on the stars, and your feet on the ground," he loved to say.

President Roosevelt

President Roosevelt and his family

TR, as his friends called him, was born in 1858 in New York City. When he was very young, he was sick with asthma. Later, he started exercising every day. He became strong and fit. He learned to love sports and the outdoors.

TR loved to read and write too. Most of all, he loved nature. When he was seven years old, he started the Roosevelt Museum of Natural History in his family's house. It was filled with bones and skins and skulls of animals he had found. His love of nature remained an important part of his life when he was president.

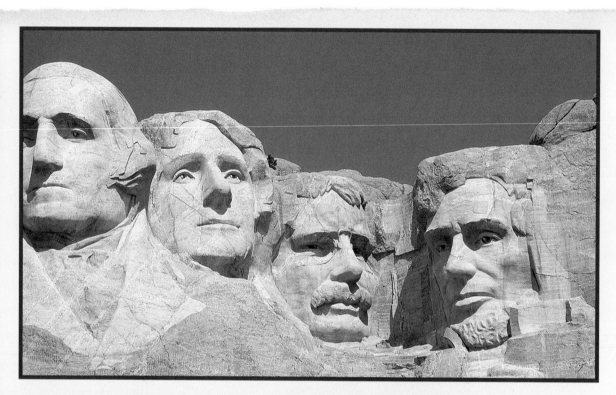

An image of Theodore Roosevelt's face is carved in stone, sixty feet high, at Mount Rushmore in South Dakota.

Theodore Roosevelt was elected vice president in 1900. When President William McKinley was killed less than a year later, TR became president. He was only forty-two years old, the youngest president ever.

Theodore Roosevelt and a friend look out on Yosemite National Park.

While TR was president, he made laws to create national forests and national parks. That's how he became known as the "Conservation President."

Theodore Roosevelt was president from 1901 to 1909. He died ten years later on January 16, 1919. He was sixty years old.

Today we can still enjoy the beautiful parks he helped create.

Theodore Roosevelt National Park, North Dakota

TR and the Teddy Bear

DID YOU KNOW THAT teddy bears are named after President Theodore Roosevelt? Some toy makers had the idea of making stuffed toy bears. They knew that President Roosevelt was interested in animals, so one of the toy makers asked for his permission to call them Teddy's bears. TR liked the bears, but he never did like the nickname "Teddy."

TEDDY BEAR

TOY CO.

OTTO SCHMIDT & SONS
NEW YORK, N.Y.

WILMA RUDOLPH

OLYMPIC TRACK CHAMPION

BY VERONICA FREEMAN ELLIS

ALL EYES WATCHED the little girl walking down the aisle. Wasn't she Wilma Rudolph, who always wore a brace on her left leg? Yes, she was. But that Sunday morning in church, Wilma was walking without her brace. Everyone was surprised, but Wilma had always known that she would walk again someday.

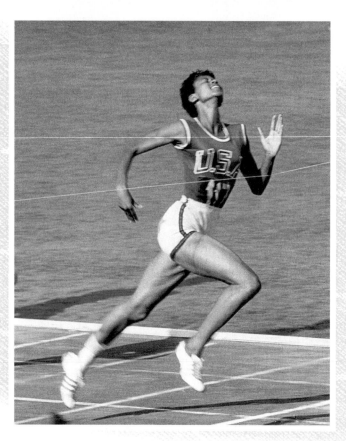

Wilma wins the 100-meter dash.

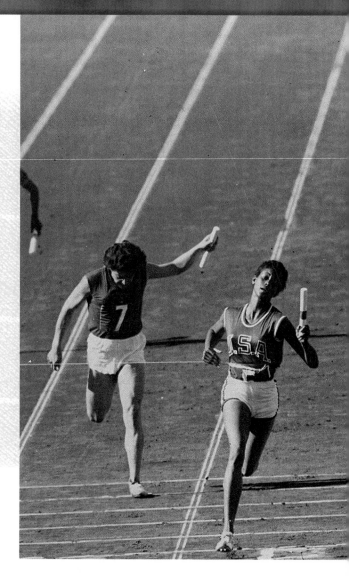

Wilma runs a 400-meter relay.

"The doctors told me I would never walk," said Wilma many years later, "but my mother told me I would, so I believed my mother."

Wilma Rudolph was born in Bethlehem, Tennessee, in 1940. Just before her fifth birthday, Wilma became very ill. Her illness caused her to lose the use of her left leg.

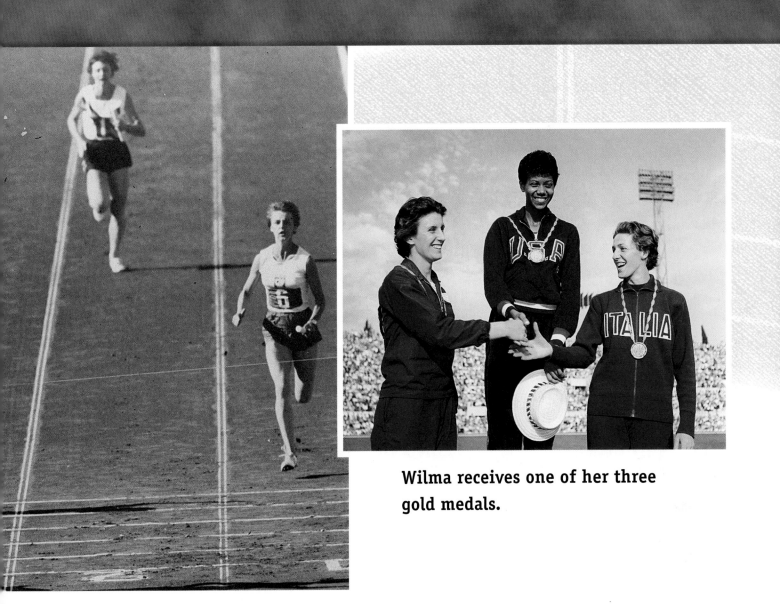

Wilma receives one of her three gold medals.

Wilma was determined to walk. She did exercises every day to make her leg stronger. Even though doctors had put a steel brace on her leg, Wilma practiced walking every day without it. When she was twelve years old, she took off her brace for good.

At sixteen, Wilma Rudolph became the youngest member of the 1956 U.S. Olympic track team. That year she won a bronze medal in the relay race.

In 1960, Wilma became world famous. At the Olympics in Rome, Italy, she won a gold medal for the 100-meter dash. She won a second gold medal for the 200-meter dash.

It was time for the 400-meter relay race. Wilma was the final runner on her team. It was up to her to cross the finish line. When her teammate handed her the baton, Wilma nearly dropped it! Her team fell to third place, but Wilma didn't give up. She ran as hard as she could — and she won.

IMPORTANT DATES AND EVENTS

1940

Wilma Rudolph is born on June 23.

1956

She wins a bronze medal at the Olympics.

1960

She wins three gold medals at the Rome Olympics.

Wilma Rudolph became the first American woman to win three gold medals in track at the same Olympics. The little girl who had been told she would never walk was now the fastest woman runner in the world!

Wilma retired from running in 1962. She became a second-grade teacher and a high school track coach. She started the Wilma Rudolph Foundation, which teaches young athletes that they, too, can be champions.

1962
Wilma retires from running.

1981
She starts the Wilma Rudolph Foundation.

1983
Wilma is elected to the U.S. Olympic Hall of Fame.

1994
She dies on November 12, in Brentwood, Tennessee.

Think About the BIOGRAPHIES

1. Ellen Ochoa tells children not to be afraid to reach for the stars. What does she mean?

2. Compare the problems that Theodore Roosevelt and Wilma Rudolph had when they were children. How did they solve their problems?

3. Which one of these people do you wish you could meet? Why?

4. What is something you have worked hard at? What helped you want to try, even though it was hard?

Internet

Take an Online Quiz

You have just read some biographies. See what you've learned by taking an online quiz.

www.eduplace.com/kids

Narrating

Write a Biography

Choose a person you want to know more about. That person might be an explorer, a president, or a sports star. Look up facts about the person in books, in the encyclopedia, or on the Internet. Write a biography of the person.

Tips

- **Write an interesting beginning for the biography.**
- **Tell about the person's early life first. Then tell about the person's later years.**
- **Write a title that will get a reader's attention.**

Former President Jimmy Carter helps build houses for people.

Yo-Yo Ma plays the cello.

Family Time

What is a family?

Who is a family?

Either a lot or a few

is a family;

But whether there's ten

or there's two in *your* family,

All of your family plus *you*

is a family!

by Mary Ann Hoberman

Family Time

with Pat Cummings

Dear Reader,

You're about to meet several families in this theme. My family means *everything* to me. My father was in the army, so we moved often. We lived in Germany, Japan, Illinois, Kansas, and Virginia. Each time we moved, I'd make new friends. Then I'd have to leave them and move again. But my family was always there for me.

I have two sisters and one brother. Their names are Linda, Barbara, and Artie. We took a lot of pictures when we were growing up. The pictures on these pages are from my family photo album. I hope you enjoy them as much as I do!

This old-fashioned car was in an Illinois museum. Since the car couldn't move, Linda and Artie let me steer!

Here are Dad and Artie, watching boats in Germany.

Once Artie got used to having a little sister, he and Barbara were a team.

Here are Mom and I when we lived in Japan. She let me explore the nearby village with my friends.

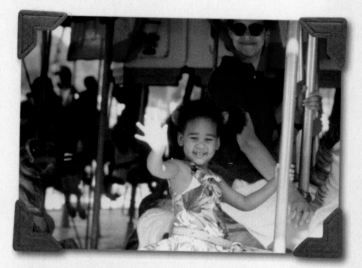

For one school play, I was a rabbit wearing shiny shoes. Linda was a grasshopper!

Now I take pictures of my family. Here are Linda and her daughter in Virginia, enjoying a ride on a carousel.

I love spending time with my family, and I'm glad you got to meet them in these pictures. Are you ready to go visiting? Just turn the page, and you'll meet the rest of the families in this theme.

Happy Reading! ☆ Pat Cummings

Special Family Time

Pat Cummings is proud to show you photos from her family photo album. Think about some photos that your family has at home. What would you tell a friend about your favorite family photo?

You will meet different families in this theme. Just like Pat Cummings and her family, there are brothers, sisters, and parents in these selections. You'll meet grandparents, too. While you are reading these family stories, think about what makes the families special.

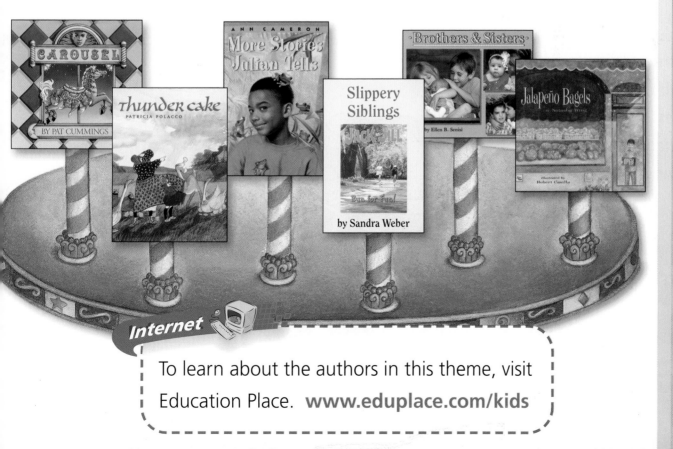

Internet

To learn about the authors in this theme, visit Education Place. **www.eduplace.com/kids**

Background and Vocabulary

Brothers and Sisters

Genre **Nonfiction**

Key Vocabulary

distract

newborn

pest

teenage

twins

Vocabulary Reader

Twins

e • Glossary

Being a Brother or Sister

What happens when a **newborn** baby enters a family? In some families, a **teenage** brother or sister may help grown-ups take care of younger children.

In the selection you're going to read next, you'll hear brothers and sisters of all ages talk about their families.

Babies and very young children need a lot of attention.

An older brother or sister can **distract** a baby so that family members can take care of other responsibilities.

Twins are twice the work, and twice as much fun!

Sometimes, a younger sister or brother can seem like a **pest**. But remember, you were a baby once too.

·Brothers & Sisters·

by Ellen B. Senisi

What is it like to have a new brother or sister?
Tori is going to find out soon. Her mother is going
to have a baby. "Is it going to be a boy or a girl?"
Tori wonders. "Will Mommy love me as much when
the baby comes?"

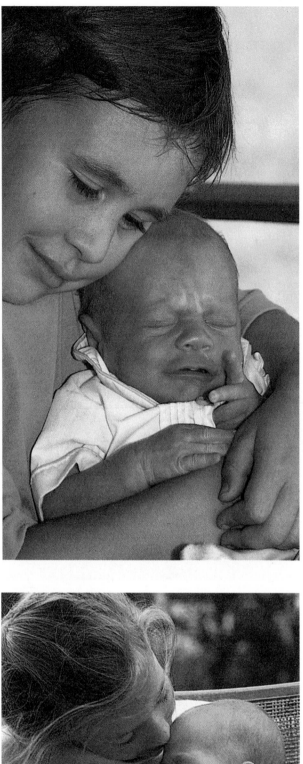

Ben has a newborn brother, and Dorrie has a new sister. Sometimes having a baby in the family is fun.

"Our new baby is so soft and tiny that I want to cuddle her all the time," says Dorrie.

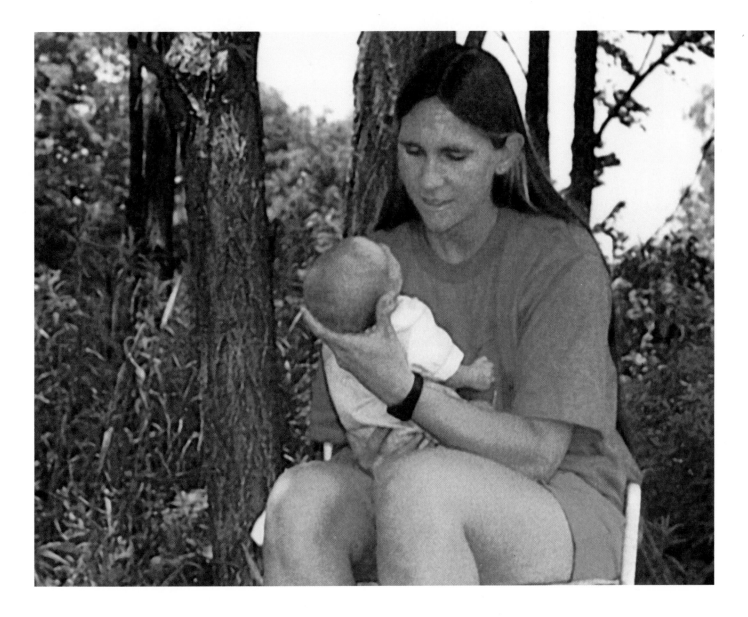

But sometimes a baby is not so much fun.

"Babies can't do anything by themselves," says Ben. "Mommy still loves me. But she is so busy taking care of the baby, I have to play by myself until he takes another nap."

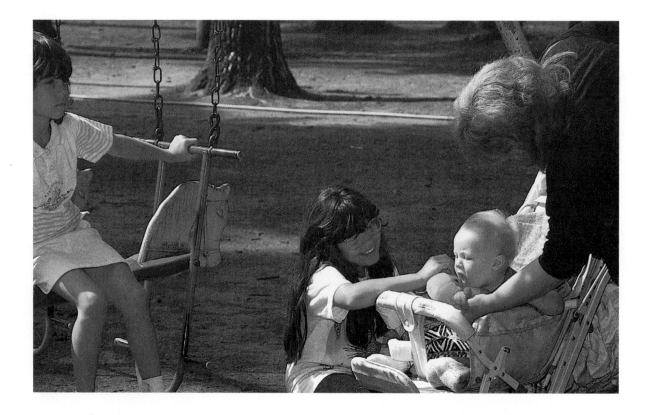

"I'm so tired of hearing everyone say how cute the baby is," says Valerie.

"I like to hold my baby sister all by myself," says Michael. So does Leo.

Jasmine and Juanita (hwa-NEE-ta) have baby sisters who have learned how to walk. "She's old enough to get into trouble now," says Jasmine, "lots of trouble."

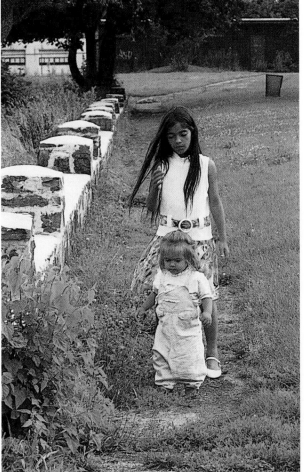

"I help distract my sister," says Juanita. "My mom says I'm the best helper with the baby."

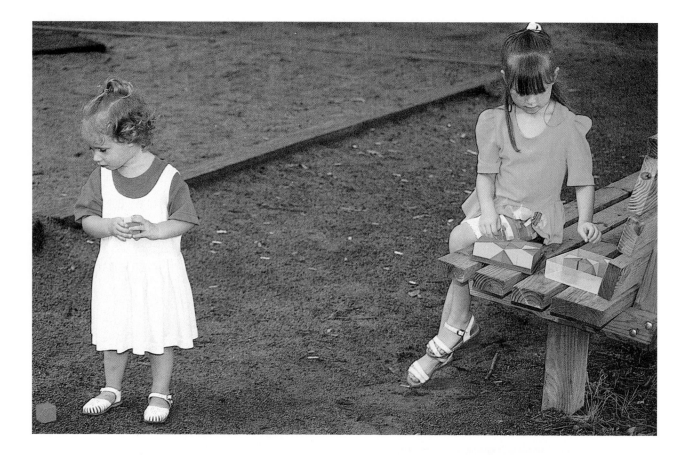

"My sister always wants to do what I'm doing, but she doesn't play games the way you're supposed to," says Alicia.

"Sometimes," says Judson, "we have so much fun together."

Rena is older than her sister. "I know things my little sister doesn't," says Rena. "Now that she is in kindergarten, I can help her get ready in the morning. And I can take her to her classroom."

"You learn to share when you have a sister," Tori says.

"It's hardest to share our parents," says Rena.

Katelyn and Jordan are almost the same age.
So are Ben and Suzannah.

"Sometimes, we're best friends,"
says Jordan.

"And sometimes we're worst enemies,"
says Katelyn.

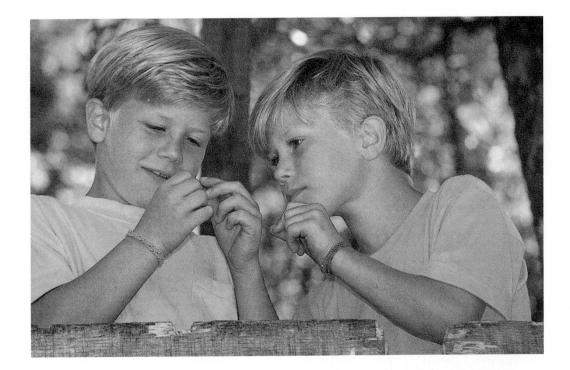

Jeremy and Jonathan are twins. "We have each other to play with all the time," says Jeremy.

Ian and Ryan are twins, too. "Dad says that we even sleep the same way," says Ryan. "We like looking so much alike that we can trick people."

"We aren't exactly alike, though," says Ian. "I'm better at drawing, but my brother is better at sports."

Sometimes it's hard to be a younger brother.

"It's not fair!" says Peter. "Just because she's older, my sister can do everything better."

And sometimes it's great to be a younger brother.

172

"She's my other mom," says Steven.

"We have our own secrets," says Tyler.

"And we have our own special games."

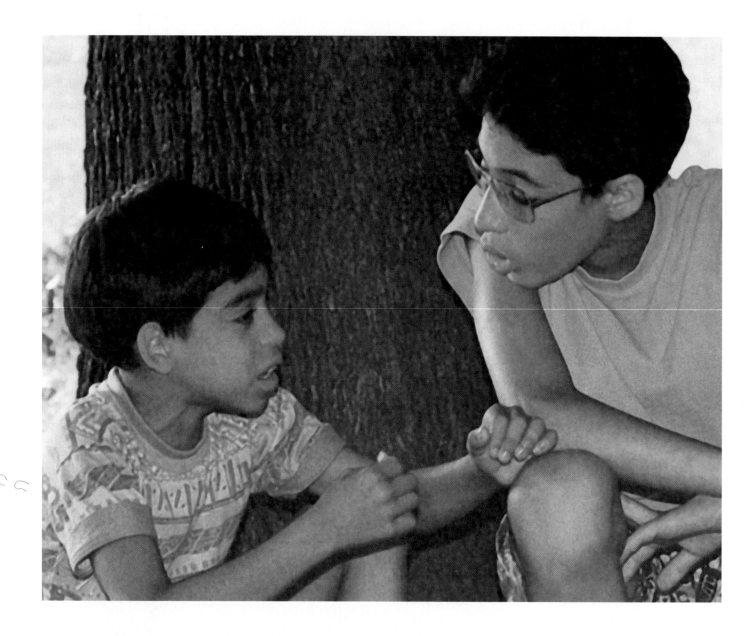

Trey's older brother and Jesse's older sister are both in middle school.

"He gets mad at me because he thinks I'm a pest," says Trey.

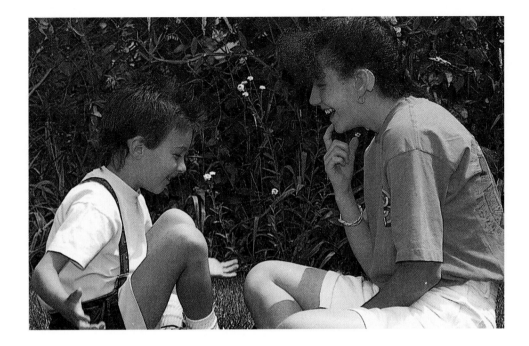

"We get mad at each other a lot," says Jesse. "But then we forget about it."

"Sometimes, my sister is the only person who understands how I feel," says Juanita.

Bianca has a teenage sister.
"When can I go everywhere and
do everything, just like her?"
Bianca wonders.

"Sometimes my sister acts like a grown-up, and
we don't have anything to talk about," says Maura.
"Other times she's just like me."

"I was adopted," says Sujathi (soo-JAH-tee). "Jessica and I came from different moms and dads. But we're still sisters — forever."

Laura and Emma were also adopted. "I tell everybody right away, 'This is my sister!'"

"My dad told me that when they were kids, he and my uncle got into fights. But they still liked each other the best," says Will. "They're grown-ups now and they help each other a lot. They let me help, too."

"My mom said she and her sister used to play school all the time. Now it's for real because they're both teachers," says Eddie. "My mom says her sister is more important to her than ever."

"My grandma and my great-aunt have been
sisters for seventy years," says Katherine. "Grandma
says her sister is still her best friend."

Meet the Author and Photographer
Ellen B. Senisi

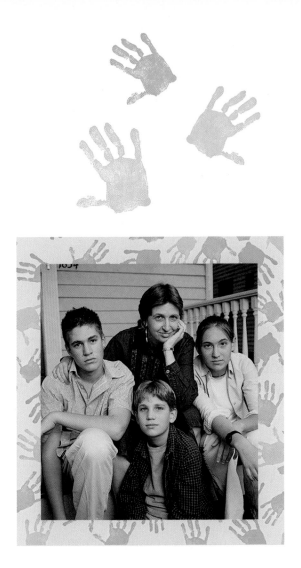

Ellen Senisi loves to put together words and photos to create books for children. One of the things that most interests her about photography is the fact that although the people or things in a photograph change, the pictures themselves always stay the same.

Look closely at the photographs in *Brothers and Sisters*. You'll see pictures she took several years ago of her three children, Will, Katherine, and Steven.

**Other books by
Ellen B. Senisi:**
*For My Family, Love, Allie
Reading Grows*

If you'd like to know more about Ellen Senisi and her work as a photographer and author of children's books, visit Education Place.

www.eduplace.com/kids

Think About the Selection

Compare two or more of the families in this selection. How are they alike? How are they different?

In what ways can an older brother or sister help a younger brother or sister? Give examples from the selection to support your answer.

How are brothers and sisters sometimes like best friends?

4. Why is having a brother or sister sometimes hard?

5. **Connecting/Comparing** What have you learned about families from reading this selection?

Creating

Write a Story

Choose a photo from the selection. Write a story about what you think the people in the photo might be thinking or saying.

Tips

- **Use a story map to help you get started.**
- **Think of an interesting title for your story.**

Identify Abilities

Choose a photo of a baby, one of someone about your age, and one of a teenager or adult. Write a description of some of the things each person you chose is able to do.

List Family Words

Work with a partner to make a list of words that name people in a family. Begin with words from the story, such as *brother* and *sister*. Add as many words as you can. Then talk about how the people you named are related to each other.

Bonus Put the words in your list in alphabetical order.

Internet

Solve a Web Hidden Message

Test what you know about brothers and sisters by solving a Web hidden message. You'll find one on Education Place. **www.eduplace.com/kids**

Genre

Poetry

Skill: How to Read a Poem

❶ Read the title of the poem.

❷ Try to predict what the poem will be about.

❸ Read the poem more than once.

❹ Compare what you first thought the poem would be about with what you think after reading it again.

Brother and Sister Poems

Do Not Enter

Warning
Do Not Enter
Stop
Wrong Way
Beware
Danger
Do Not Trespass
Caution
Don't You Dare

I taped the signs onto the door —
I thought that's all I'd need.

My brother came in anyway —
He's never learned to read.

by Florence Parry Heide and Roxanne Heide Pierce

I Did Not Eat Your Ice Cream

I did not eat your ice cream,
I did not swipe your socks.
I did not stuff your lunch box
with rubber bands and rocks.

I did not hide your sweater,
I did not dent your bike,
it must have been my sister,
we look a lot alike.

by Jack Prelutsky

little sister

holds on tight.

My hands hurt

from all that squeezing,

but I don't mind.

She thinks no one will bother her

when I'm around,

and they won't

if I can help it.

And even when I can't,

I try

'cause she believes in me.

by Nikki Grimes

187

A Personal Narrative

A personal narrative is a true story about something that happened to the writer. Use this student's writing as a model when you write a personal narrative of your own.

My New Kite

A good **beginning** tells what the narrative is about.

One windy day I got a new kite. I had not flown a kite in a long time. My dad took me to a big field to fly it. When we opened the package, a big gust of wind blew the instructions away. My dad had to figure out how to put the kite together. It wasn't easy because the wind kept blowing everything, but we got it put together.

Good writers stay on the **topic**.

Then my dad let me hold the kite in my hand. A huge gust of wind came by. I let go of my kite, held onto the string, and the kite went with the wind way up in the sky. I kept on letting more and more string out until all the string was out. My kite was so high I could hardly see it. I thought that it looked like a tiny dot.

Suddenly, it got close to a tree. I pulled it in the opposite direction. My kite was in trouble. To make matters worse, it started to rain. As I reeled my kite in, it started to pour. I saved my kite just in time.

I can't wait for the next windy day to fly my kite again.

Details help the reader picture what happened.

A good **ending** wraps up the narrative.

Meet the Author

Roy H.

Grade: two
State: Delaware
Hobbies: drawing, riding his bike
What he'd like to be when he grows up: an illustrator

Background and Vocabulary

Jalapeño Bagels

Genre: **Realistic Fiction**

Key Vocabulary

bakery

cultures

customers

dough

ingredients

recipes

Vocabulary Reader

Welcome to the Bakery

e • Glossary

190

Inside a Bakery

Have you ever stepped inside a **bakery** and smelled fresh bread baking? Have you wondered how bread is made? You'll find out more about what happens in a bakery in the next story. You'll even read two **recipes** for baking.

▼ Bakers prepare their **dough** and bake it early in the day, usually before sunrise, so that **customers** may have the freshest bread possible.

▲ The **ingredients** may change, but the idea is the same: everyone loves a treat from the bakery.

◄ Most **cultures** around the world eat breads or baked goods. Almost all bread recipes use some sort of flour and water. The rest is up to the baker.

Meet the Author
Natasha Wing

Fact File
Favorite Children's Books:
The Polar Express, Charlie and the Chocolate Factory, The Cat in the Hat, The Golden Compass
Favorite Season: Fall
Favorite Color: Cranberry red
Favorite Cookie: Oatmeal raisin with vanilla chips

Other books by Natasha Wing:
Hippity Hop, Frog on Top
The Night Before Easter

Like Pablo in *Jalapeño Bagels*, Robert Casilla's son, Robert, Jr., speaks both English and Spanish. In fact, Mr. Casilla sometimes uses Robert Jr. as a model for his drawings and illustrations.

Meet the Illustrator
Robert Casilla

Other books illustrated by Robert Casilla:
The Little Painter of Sabana Grande
A Picture Book of Rosa Parks

Internet

To find out more about Natasha Wing and Robert Casilla, visit Education Place. **www.eduplace.com/kids**

Jalapeño Bagels

by Natasha Wing

illustrated by
Robert Casilla

Strategy Focus

A boy and his family are getting ready for an
important event at school. Read the selection carefully,
and think of **questions** to ask about their plans.

193

194

"What should I bring to school on Monday for International Day?" I ask my mother. "My teacher told us to bring something from our culture."

"You can bring a treat from the *panadería*," she suggests. Panadería is what Mamá calls our bakery. "Help us bake on Sunday — then you can pick out whatever you want."

"It's a deal," I tell her. I like helping at the bakery. It's warm there, and everything smells so good.

Early Sunday morning, when it is still dark, my
mother wakes me up.

"Pablo, it's time to go to work," she says.

We walk down the street to the bakery. My father
turns on the lights. My mother turns on the ovens. She
gets out the pans and ingredients for *pan dulce* (pahn
DOOL-seh). Pan dulce is Mexican sweet bread.

I help my mother mix and knead the dough. She
shapes rolls and loaves of bread and slides them into the
oven. People tell her she makes the best pan dulce in
town.

"Maybe I'll bring pan dulce to school," I tell her.

Next we make *empanadas de calabaza* — pumpkin turnovers. I'm in charge of spooning the pumpkin filling. Mamá folds the dough in half and presses the edges with a fork. She bakes them until they are flaky and golden brown. Some customers come to our bakery just for her turnovers.

"Maybe I'll bring empanadas de calabaza instead."

"You'll figure it out," she says. "Ready to make *chango* bars?"

Mamá lets me pour in the chocolate chips and nuts. When she's not looking, I pour in more chocolate chips.

"I could bring chango bars. They're my favorite dessert."

"Mine, too" says Mamá. "This batch should be especially good. I put in extra chips."

My father calls from the back room. "Pablo! Come help me with the bagels!" Papá speaks English and Yiddish. He learned Yiddish from his family in New York City. I know some words, too. *Bubbe* means "grandmother." He uses my bubbe's recipe to make the bagels.

First he makes the dough in a big metal bowl. Then he rolls it out into a long rope shape. He cuts off pieces and shows me how to connect the ends in a circle. We put the circles on trays where they sit and rise.

While we are waiting my father makes *challah*, Jewish braided bread. He lets me practice braiding challah dough at my own counter. It's a lot like braiding hair. The customers say it is almost too beautiful to eat.

"Maybe I'll bring a loaf of challah to school," I tell Papá. He smiles.

When the bagel dough has risen, he boils the bagels in a huge pot of water and fishes them out with a long slotted spoon. I sprinkle on poppy seeds and sesame seeds, and then they go in the oven.

"Maybe I could bring sesame-seed bagels with cream cheese."

"No *lox?*" Lox is smoked salmon. My father's favorite bagel is pumpernickel with a smear of cream cheese and lox.

I crinkle my nose. "Lox tastes like fish. Jam is better."

My mother joins us and helps my father make another batch of bagels — *jalapeño* (ha-la-PEN-yo) bagels. My parents use their own special recipe. While Papá kneads the dough, Mamá chops the jalapeño *chiles*. She tosses them into the dough and adds dried red peppers. We roll, cut, make circles, and let them rise. I can't wait until they are done because I am getting hungry.

"Have you decided what you're going to bring to school?" asks Mamá.

"It's hard to choose. Everything is so good," I tell her. I look at Papá. "Except for lox."

"You should decide before we open," warns Mamá,
"or else our customers will buy everything up."

I walk past all the sweet breads, chango bars,
and bagels.

I think about my mother and my father and all the
different things they make in the bakery.

And suddenly I know exactly what I'm going to bring.

"Jalapeño bagels," I tell my parents. "And I'll spread them with cream cheese and jam."

"Why jalapeño bagels?" asks Papá.

"Because they are a mixture of both of you. Just like me!"

These recipes are from a real Mexican-Jewish-American bakery, Los Bagels Bakery & Cafe, in Arcata, California. Kids should ask grown-ups for help with both recipes.

Chango Bars

$\frac{1}{2}$ cup butter

$\frac{1}{2}$ cup margarine

2 cups brown sugar

3 eggs

$2\frac{1}{3}$ cups flour

1 tablespoon baking powder

1 teaspoon salt

1 cup chocolate chips

1 cup mixed nuts

Melt butter and margarine. While this is melting, cream brown sugar and eggs, then add melted butter and margarine. Combine flour, baking powder, and salt and stir into sugar mixture. Fold in chocolate chips and nuts. Pour mixture into greased 9 inch x 13 inch baking pan and bake 45 to 50 minutes at 350 degrees.

For this recipe you will need lots of time. But these bagels are worth the wait!

Jalapeño Bagels

$1\frac{3}{4}$ cups lukewarm water

$\frac{1}{2}$ teaspoon dry yeast

2 teaspoons salt

$1\frac{1}{2}$ tablespoons sugar

5 to 6 cups flour

$\frac{1}{3}$ cup jalapeños, chopped

$\frac{1}{4}$ cup dried red peppers

Mix water, yeast, salt, and sugar. Add flour and jalapeños and mix into a ball. Knead for 10 to 12 minutes, adding more flour if necessary, until dough is stiff. Add red peppers and knead for 3 minutes. Let dough rest 10 minutes, then cut into 12 pieces with a knife.

Roll each piece of dough on a table to form long tube-like shapes. Then, for each of the twelve pieces, connect the two ends by overlapping them about $\frac{3}{4}$ of an inch and rolling the ends together to make a ring shape. Make sure each joint is secure or it will come apart while boiling.

Cover with a damp towel and let rise 1 to $1\frac{1}{2}$ hours in a warm spot. In a large pot, bring 1 to 2 gallons of water to a rolling boil. Place bagels in boiling water and boil until they float (15 to 30 seconds). Remove with a slotted spoon and place on a lightly greased cookie sheet. Bake at 400 degrees for 10 to 15 minutes or until golden brown.

Think About the Selection

1. Why are jalapeño bagels a good choice of food for Pablo to take to school for International Day?

2. What do you think might be fun about having a family business? What might be difficult?

3. Which of the foods described in the story do you think you'd like best? Why?

4. Pablo is helpful in several ways at the panadería. In what ways can you be helpful at home or in your classroom?

5. **Connecting/Comparing** If Pablo had a younger brother or sister, what might he tell him or her about their family?

Explaining

Write a How-to Paragraph

Think of a food you know how to make. Write a paragraph that explains how to make it. Begin by telling what you are going to make. Then tell step-by-step how to make it.

Tips

- Start by making a list of ingredients.
- Use time-order words such as *first, next,* and *then.*

Compare Measurements

Look at the recipes for chango bars and jalapeño bagels on pages 211–213. Then answer these questions.

- Which recipe uses more flour?

- Which recipe uses more salt? How much more?

- Which recipe uses more sugar?

Bonus Write two more questions about the recipes. Ask a classmate to answer them.

Social Studies

Make an International Day Poster

Plan your own school or classroom International Day with a small group. Think of favorite family foods. Then make a poster to advertise International Day. Include the foods you chose on your poster.

Internet

Solve a Web Word Scramble

Learn more about baking and bakeries when you solve a Web word scramble on Education Place.

www.eduplace.com/kids

Welcome to the Kitchen

by Carolyn E. Moore, Mimi Kerr, and Robert Shulman

The kitchen is the best place to be when it comes to good food. The cooking is fun and so is the eating. You can make snacks, meals, special holiday treats for yourself and for your whole family.

If you haven't done much cooking before, you should have an adult with you who can show you how to use kitchen equipment.

Safety First

1. Dress safely. Roll up long sleeves and pull your hair back so nothing gets into the food that doesn't belong there. Wear an apron so food doesn't get where it doesn't belong.

2. Keep your fingers away from the sharp edge of a knife. Pick knives up by the handle, not by the blade. Always cut food on a cutting board, not while holding food in your hand.

3. Make sure electric appliances are turned off before you plug them in.

4. Use pot holders or hot pads when you pick up pots from the stove or put things in or take things out of the oven.

5. Don't let the handles of pots stick out over the side of the stove where someone could bump into them.

6. Turn the oven or stove burner off as soon as you have finished with it.

Background and Vocabulary

Carousel

Genre **Realistic Fiction**

Key Vocabulary

angry
fussed
groaned
grumbled
grumpily
promised

Vocabulary Reader

The Joke Book

e • Glossary

A BAD DAY

Have you ever **grumbled** at someone, even though you weren't really mad at them? Or have you **fussed** and argued when you were tired, or **groaned** when you broke a favorite toy? Everyone has bad days now and then.

People sometimes get **angry**, or act **grumpily**, when they're having a bad day. In the story you are about to read, a girl is upset when someone can't do what he **promised** he would do. Find out what lessons she learns from her own bad day.

Meet the Author and Illustrator
Pat Cummings

Fact File

Birthday: November 9

Favorite children's books:
The Chronicles of Narnia
by C.S. Lewis

How she makes her art:
She has used all kinds of
materials to make her books,
including watercolors, acrylics,
wallpaper, and rubber stamps.

Her favorite illustrators:
Lane Smith, Chris Van
Allsburg, Floyd Cooper,
and Lois Ehlert

Pets: She has a cat
named Cash.

Other Books:

*Petey Moroni's Camp
Runamok Diary*

Clean Your Room, Harvey Moon

Storm in the Night

Internet

It you liked reading *Carousel*, and want to read
more about Pat Cummings, visit our Web site.
www.eduplace.com/kids

CAROUSEL

BY PAT CUMMINGS

Strategy Focus

A little girl's birthday turns into a bad day. As you read the story, try to **predict** how it will end.

Alex didn't want her hair braided or her shiny
shoes buckled or every single little pearly button
buttoned on her dress. And she definitely didn't want
her birthday cake after dinner with just her aunts.

"Where's Daddy?" she grumbled for the eighth time.
"Hold still, Alex," sighed her mother, tugging away.
Off went the sneakers. On went the bows. Off went
the jeans. On came the frills.

Dinner lasted forever. Alex pushed peas from side to side on her plate. She stabbed a potato chunk with her fork, dragged it through the gravy, and ate it like an ice-cream cone.

"Alex," her mother warned, and then smiled at the aunts. "Let's open your presents before we cut the cake."

Before Alex could say, "Let's wait for Daddy," her
aunts had whisked away the dinner dishes, pulled
balloons out of bags, and popped party hats on
everyone's heads. There was a pile of presents to open.

Alex opened Auntie Lea's gift first. "I have a
million pairs of pajamas," she mumbled grumpily.

She unwrapped a frothy ballerina tutu from Aunt Ruby. Aunt Ruby liked things to sparkle. "Looks scratchy," Alex fussed under her breath. Her mother made a face at her, but Alex didn't care.

Then, burrowing through puffs of tissues, Alex found a pair of long, fuzzy, hot pink slipper-socks. They had rabbit ears and googly eyes and WHISKERS! Aunt Rose scurried to grab her camera.

"No way," Alex groaned.

"Alex!" her mother said sharply. "Maybe you need to go to bed." Alex quickly hugged her aunts and thanked them. She wasn't mad at *them*. "But Daddy promised . . ." she began.

"He said he'd try, honey. And," her mother added, handing her the last gift, "he said to give you this just in case he didn't get back from his trip in time."

Alex felt her cheeks getting hot. *He knew he wouldn't be home!* She tugged at the paper and yanked off the ribbons.

"Ooooooohhh . . . aaaaaahhhh!" the aunts cried. There before her was the most perfect little carousel that Alex had ever seen.

"He said he'd be here!" Alex hissed angrily. The aunts stopped ooooohing. "He promised!" She kicked away the ribbons at her feet.

"That's it, young lady! No cake for you. Say good-night." Her mother wasn't smiling.

But Alex didn't care. She wanted to blow the candy roses right off the cake anyway. "Good-NIGHT!" Alex barked. She marched upstairs holding the carousel by one of its delicate little poles.

"I don't care." Alex twisted the bows out of her
hair and pulled off her party dress without stopping to
undo a single little button. "He knew it. He knew it,"
she fussed at the little animals.

Alex heard her aunts laughing downstairs.
"They're eating up my cake!"

She jumped into bed, kicked the blankets back, and sent the carousel tumbling. There was a soft snap. Slowly, she picked up the carousel and studied it. The tiny zebra looked wobbly. With just a wiggle, it broke off completely!

Its little painted face looked almost angry. She had to fix the carousel before her father came home, or he would think she didn't like her gift. She yawned. She turned. There would be time in the morning. . . .

Alex didn't remember falling asleep. Something tickled her knee, waking her in time to see the last of the carousel animals hopping lightly out of her window.

"Oh, no," she gasped. They had to come back.
The empty carousel was on its side, all deserted and
sad-looking. "Daddy," she whispered.

Alex ran to the window, and, knowing what
she had to do, slipped easily down into the soft
grass outside.

The animals
were getting away! Alex took
off running. Even as she hurried after
them, it seemed that the
moonlight was making
them grow, their legs
stretching farther and
farther. A paw here, ears
there, whiskers in and out
of the blue nighttime
leaves.

And just when she
thought she had lost them forever,
Alex saw them waiting beyond the tall trees.
They were waiting for her.
Alex tiptoed up to the zebra. She carefully
climbed up on his back. A little bit of pole was
sticking up just where she had broken it off.
"Sorry," she whispered in his ear. Had he
heard her?
The zebra shook his mane and
began to trot. Then he galloped,
then he flew.

Around
and around and
around, all of the animals were
running with him. From frog to
flamingo, from rabbit to giraffe, Alex
took turns: upside down, right
side up, one hand, no hands,
both eyes closed.

When at last they slowed down,
Alex found she was again on the zebra's
back. One by one, the sleepy animals made
their way through the cool grass toward her
bedroom window. Alex curled her fingers in
and out of the zebra's mane. Even in
the pale light, she could see that
he was smiling.

One eye opened. Then the other. It was morning.

"Oh, dear!" Alex sat straight up. She remembered everything. She remembered the carousel animals had all gotten loose.

She pulled the covers apart, but now there wasn't a single little animal in sight. She rolled onto the floor and peered under the bed. No flamingo. No leopard. Nothing!

"Happy birthday, sleepyhead. You awake?" Her father was home! Hugging Alex, he kissed her smack on the nose. Then he saw the carousel sitting underneath the window.

"Daddy, I'm sorry I broke it," Alex said.

"And I'm sorry I missed your birthday," her father answered. "I got really angry when my plane was so late in coming home. But I couldn't stay angry. Know why?"

Alex shook her head.

"Because the same thing that made me angry made me happy when I thought about it. I was happy just to be coming home."

"Breakfast, anyone?" her mother asked, going straight to the window to close it. "It got a bit windy in here last night." She winked at Alex.

Alex kissed them both.

"We have a little work to do," her dad said, pressing the tiny zebra into Alex's hand. "What's for breakfast?"

"Oh, scrambled cake and ice-cream omelettes." Her mother laughed and headed downstairs.

Alex took her dad by the hand.

"And put on those cute little slippers for Daddy, Alex!" her mother called out.

Alex squeezed her dad's hand. He was going to *love* those slippers!

Think About the Selection

1. How do you think Alex felt about her behavior the day after her party?

2. How do you think Alex's dad felt about missing her birthday party?

3. What do you think happened to Alex between the time she went to bed and the time she woke up in the morning?

4. How might you feel if you broke a special gift that you liked very much?

5. Connecting/Comparing Compare Pablo in *Jalapeño Bagels* to Alex. In what ways are they alike? How are they different?

Narrating

Write a Personal Narrative

Alex's father gave her a very special gift. Think of a gift that you've given or received. Compare your memorable gift to Alex's carousel. Write a story about your gift.

Tips

- Make sure the events in your story are in order.
- Write the word *I* with a capital letter.

Design a Carousel Animal

Choose an animal from the story, or think of a favorite animal. Use crayons or markers to draw and color your animal. With a group, make a carousel from cut paper, and place your animals on your carousel.

Practice Politeness

Alex did not thank her aunts properly for their gifts. Take turns with a classmate. Role-play Alex thanking an aunt. Tell about the gift and explain why you enjoyed it.

Internet

Build a Story

Do you think you know the story inside-out and backwards? Test your knowledge of *Carousel*. Visit Education Place and unscramble our mixed-up story.

www.eduplace.com/kids

Genre

Magazine Article

Skill: How to Read a Magazine Article

❶ Read the title and headings to identify the topic.

❷ Think about what you already know about the topic.

❸ Look at photos and captions.

❹ Go back and carefully read the article.

Carousel
Designed by Kids

by Kathy Kranking, from Ranger Rick magazine

Have you ever drawn a picture of your favorite animal? Imagine if someone built an exact copy of your drawing — and made it big enough for you to ride. That's what happened to the drawings of a bunch of lucky kids in New York City. And now the kids can ride their animals any time they want!

The animals are all part of the Totally Kid Carousel in New York's Riverbank State Park. It's the first carousel in the world designed by kids.

So how did it all come about? The wizard behind this magical idea is an artist named Milo Mottola. The city officials wanted an artist to build a carousel in the park. They asked Milo to come up with ideas.

Milo thought for a long time. Then he saw a young friend draw a horse. "That's it!" Milo said. "I could ask kids to draw funny, lumpy carousel animals. They would be charming and wonderful too!"

So Milo talked to lots and lots of kids in the neighborhood around Riverbank State Park. Most were first and second graders. He got them to make drawings of their favorite animals.

Then Milo had a hard job to do. Only 36 animals would fit on the carousel. So he had to pick from a thousand drawings the kids had done. Finally the choices were made.

How did each animal go from a drawing to a carousel critter? Here's what happened with this deer, drawn by Edwin Vargas.

How they're made

Lizzie Queena Castle shows off her carousel horse. See how much it looks like her drawing? The carousel animals show what happens when you take a good idea — and give it a whirl!

257

Thunder Cake

Genre **Realistic Fiction**

Key Vocabulary

bolt
horizon
lightning
rumbled
thunder
weather

Vocabulary Reader

A Thunderstorm Is Coming!

by Margie Sigman

e • Glossary

Thunder and Lightning

You have probably heard **thunder** as it **rumbled** during a storm. Thunder is the loud noise that you hear after you see a flash of **lightning**.

Lightning is a quick flash or **bolt** of electricity that lights up the sky during a thunderstorm. Thunderstorms often happen when the **weather** is warm.

In the story you are about to read, a grandmother helps a little girl get over her fear of thunderstorms.

The next time you see a thunderstorm on the **horizon**, you can stay safe if you remain inside your house or in a car.

Meet the
Author and Illustrator
Patricia Polacco

Storytelling has always been a favorite tradition in Patricia Polacco's family. So it's only natural that she would become a great storyteller herself. *Thunder Cake* is a story based on Ms. Polacco's memories of life on her grandmother's farm in Michigan.

Patricia Polacco writes her stories in her house, which she named "Meteor Ridge." Her art supplies won't all fit in her home office, so she has a studio in another house a block away, just for illustrating!

Other books by Patricia Polacco:

*My Rotten Redheaded
   Older Brother*
Rechenka's Eggs
Meteor!

Internet

Patricia Polacco spends a lot of time in her studio, working on her books. To find out how she makes her illustrations, visit Education Place. **www.eduplace.com/kids**

thunder cake

PATRICIA POLACCO

⭐ **Strategy Focus**

While you read about a young girl's fear of
thunderstorms, **monitor** your understanding.
If you have questions, stop and reread to **clarify**.

Grandma looked at the horizon, drew a deep breath and said, "This is Thunder Cake baking weather, all right. Looks like a storm coming to me."

"Child, you come out from under that bed. It's only thunder you're hearing," my grandma said.

266

The air was hot, heavy, and damp. A loud clap of thunder shook the house, rattled the windows, and made me grab her close.

"Steady, child," she cooed. "Unless you let go of me, we won't be able to make a Thunder Cake today!"

"Thunder Cake?" I stammered as I hugged her even closer.

"Don't pay attention to that old thunder, except to see how close the storm is getting. When you see the lightning, start counting . . . real slow. When you hear the thunder, stop counting. That number is how many miles away the storm is. Understand?" she asked. "We need to know how far away the storm is, so we have time to make the cake and get it into the oven before the storm comes, or it won't be real Thunder Cake."

Her eyes surveyed the black clouds a way off in the distance. Then she strode into the kitchen. Her worn hands pulled a thick book from the shelf above the woodstove.

"Let's find that recipe, child," she crowed as she lovingly fingered the grease-stained pages to a creased spot.

"Here it is . . . Thunder Cake!"

She carefully penned the ingredients on a piece of notepaper. "Now let's gather all the things we'll need!" she exclaimed as she scurried toward the back door.

We were by the barn door when a huge bolt of lightning flashed. I started counting, like Grandma told me to, "1–2–3–4–5–6–7–8–9–10."

269

Then the thunder ROARED!

"Ten miles . . . it's ten miles away," Grandma said as she looked at the sky. "About an hour away, I'd say. You'll have to hurry, child. Gather them eggs careful-like," she said.

Eggs from mean old Nellie Peck hen. I was scared. I knew she would try to peck me.

"I'm here, she won't hurt you. Just get them eggs," Grandma said softly.

The lightning flashed again.

"1–2–3–4–5–6–7–8–9" I counted.

"Nine miles," Grandma reminded me.

Milk was next. Milk from old Kick Cow. As Grandma milked her, Kick Cow turned and looked mean, right at me. I was scared. She looked so big.

ZIP went the lightning. "1–2–3–4–5–6–7–8" I counted.

BAROOOOOOOOM went the thunder.

"Eight miles, child," Grandma croaked. "Now we have to get chocolate and sugar and flour from the dry shed."

I was scared as we walked down the path from the farmhouse through Tangleweed Woods to the dry shed. Suddenly the lightning slit the sky!

"1–2–3–4–5–6–7" I counted.

BOOOOOOM BA-BOOOOOOM, crashed the thunder. It scared me a lot, but I kept walking with Grandma.

Another jagged edge of lightning flashed as I crept into the dry shed! "1–2–3–4–5–6" I counted. CRACKLE, CRACKLE BOOOOOOM, KA-BOOOOOM, the thunder bellowed. It was dark and I was scared.

"I'm here, child," Grandma said softly from the doorway. "Hurry now, we haven't got much time. We've got everything but the secret ingredient."

"Three overripe tomatoes and some strawberries," Grandma whispered as she squinted at the list.

I climbed up high on the trellis. The ground looked a long way down. I was scared.

"I'm here, child," she said. Her voice was steady and soft. "You won't fall."

I reached three luscious tomatoes while she picked strawberries. Lightning again!

"1–2–3–4–5" I counted.

KA-BANG BOOOOOOOOOAROOOOM, the thunder growled.

We hurried back to the house and the warm
kitchen, and we measured the ingredients. I poured
them into the mixing bowl while Grandma mixed. I
churned butter for the frosting and melted chocolate.
Finally, we poured the batter into the cake pans and
put them into the oven together.

Lightning lit the kitchen! I only counted to three
and the thunder RRRRUMBLED and CRASHED.

"Three miles away," Grandma said, "and the
cake is in the oven. We made it! We'll have a real
Thunder Cake!"

As we waited for the cake, Grandma looked out the window for a long time. "Why, you aren't afraid of thunder. You're too brave!" she said as she looked right at me.

"I'm not brave, Grandma," I said. "I was under the bed! Remember?"

"But you got out from under it," she answered, "and you got eggs from mean old Nellie Peck Hen, you got milk from old Kick Cow, you went through Tangleweed Woods to the dry shed, you climbed the trellis in the barnyard. From where I sit, only a very brave person could have done all them things!"

283

284

I thought and thought as the storm rumbled closer. She was right. I was brave!

"Brave people can't be afraid of a sound, child," she said as we spread out the tablecloth and set the table. When we were done, we hurried into the kitchen to take the cake out of the oven. After the cake had cooled, we frosted it.

Just then the lightning flashed, and this time it lit the whole sky.

Even before the last flash had faded, the thunder ROLLED, BOOOOMED, CRASHED, and BBBBAAAAARRRROOOOOOOMMMMMMMMMMED just above us. The storm was here!

"Perfect," Grandma cooed, "just perfect." She beamed as she added the last strawberry to the glistening chocolate frosting on top of our Thunder Cake.

As rain poured down on our roof, Grandma cut a wedge for each of us. She poured us steaming cups of tea from the samovar.

When the thunder ROARED above us so hard it shook the windows and rattled the dishes in the cupboards, we just smiled and ate our Thunder Cake.

From that time on, I never feared the voice of thunder again.

My Grandma's Thunder Cake

Cream together, one at a time

1 cup shortening

$1\frac{3}{4}$ cup sugar

1 teaspoon vanilla

3 eggs, separated

(Blend yolks in. Beat whites
until they are stiff, then fold in.)

1 cup cold water

$\frac{1}{3}$ cup pureed tomatoes

Sift together

$2\frac{1}{2}$ cups cake flour

$\frac{1}{2}$ cup dry cocoa

$1\frac{1}{2}$ teaspoons baking soda

1 teaspoon salt

Mix dry mixture into creamy mixture.

Bake in two greased and floured $8\frac{1}{2}$-inch round pans
at 350° for 35 to 40 minutes.

Frost with chocolate butter frosting. Top with strawberries.

Think About the Selection

1. Why do you suppose Grandma wants the little girl to go outside?

2. How do you think Grandma learned not to be afraid during a thunderstorm?

3. What does the author do to make you feel that a storm is coming?

4. Why do you think Patricia Polacco decided to share this story?

5. **Connecting/Comparing** How is food important in *Jalapeño Bagels* and *Thunder Cake*?

Creating

Write an Acrostic Poem

Choose a storm word from the story. Write the word down the left-hand side of a piece of paper. Use the letters of the word you chose to begin the first word of each line of your poem.

Tips

- Make a list of words that begin with each letter to help you get started.
- Your poem does not need to rhyme.

Science

Compare Temperatures

Place a thermometer outside on asphalt in a sunny place. Wait three minutes, then record the temperature. Next, place the thermometer on grass. Record the temperature after three minutes. Compare the temperatures.

Tips

- Use a T-chart to record your information.
- Use a timer to keep track of the time.

Viewing

Identify Feelings

How does the girl feel about thunder when the story begins? Find a picture that shows that feeling. Then find another picture that shows how she feels later. With a partner, talk about details that make the two pictures different.

Internet

Complete a Web Word Jumble

All of the thunder cake ingredients are mixed up! Visit Education Place to solve this scrambled puzzle.

www.eduplace.com/kids

Sun and Ice

From *Out of the Bag: The Paper Bag Players Book of Plays*

Characters:	**Girl** (Narrator)**, Sun, Ice, Seed, Cloud**

Girl: Winter, spring, summer, fall.
Winter, spring, summer, fall.

Ice: *(Enters)* Not this year.

Girl: This year winter refused to leave. *(Exits)*

Ice: Why should it? The whole world is cold and white and beautiful. Lakes are frozen. Mountains are covered with snow. Icicles hang from the trees. Winter is the most powerful force on Earth.

Sun: *(Enters)* With one exception.

Ice: It's the sun! He's going to ruin everything.

Sun: You've made everything cold, hard, and still — but I'm going to warm things up, make them move and grow. *(As they argue, Ice tries to cover Sun, and Sun tries to cover Ice.)*

Ice: I make snow and blizzards.

Sun: I make it hot.

Ice: I make it cold.

Sun: Hot.

Ice: Cold. *(Sound of thunder from offstage)*

Sun: Thunder! *(Cloud enters.)*

Seed: *(Enters)* Where, where, where can I find a spot to plant myself?

Sun: What is it?

Cloud: It's a seed.

Seed: I'm looking for a place to get started, but the ground is so cold and hard! Sun, can't you warm things up — just a bit?

Sun: (*Moving close to Cloud*) Excuse me, Cloud, this little seed needs me.

Seed: (*To Sun*) What's Ice doing here? He shouldn't be here.

Sun: You heard her, Ice. It's time for you to go. (*Now Sun feels very powerful and chases Ice around the stage.*)

Sun: Melt!

Ice: I'm going, but I'll be back. (*Exits*)

Sun: (*To Seed*) Now you can start growing.

Seed: Just in time. My roots are itching and my leaves are ready to pop. I've got to grow, I just can't stop. I need some sun.

Sun: The sun is here. (*Makes a circular movement around Seed, suggesting sun rays*) How's that?

Seed: I feel dry.

Cloud: You need rain.

Sun: *(Circling Seed)* Sun.

Cloud: Rain.

Sun: How's that feel?

Seed: That feels just right.

Sun: I think it's time. Come on,
little seed, you can do it.
Come on, you're almost there.
Come on. *(Flower is fully opened.)*
Well done, little flower!

Cloud: Oh, little flower, you look
pretty good. I'm done in.
I'm all wiped out.
(Exits with a heavy, weary walk)

Sun: The seed has become a flower,
and it's a beautiful day.

The End

Check Your Progress

You have met lots of families in this theme. Now you will read two more family stories and compare them with the other selections.

On page 156, Pat Cummings says that her family means everything to her. Now think about the characters in this theme. How do they show that the people in their families are important to them?

Get ready to meet two more families. As you read, think about how the family members help each other.

Read and Compare

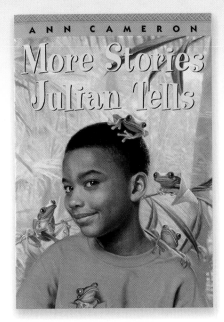

See what happens when Julian tries to send a message in a bottle.

Realistic Fiction

Try these strategies:
Compare and Contrast
Predict and Infer

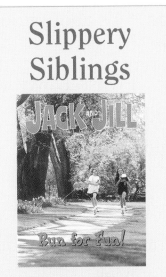

by Sandra Weber

Nonfiction

Find out how a brother and sister win a gold medal.

Try these strategies:
Monitor and Clarify
Summarize

Strategies in Action *Look for ways to use all your reading strategies as you read the selections.*

A Curve in the River

by Ann Cameron
illustrated by Gail Piazza

**Julian has an exciting idea. He puts a message inside a bottle
and throws it in the river. He hopes that his bottle will float
all the way around the world! Julian can't wait to find out if
someone far away gets his message.**

"Julian," Gloria said, "it's about your bottle with the
message — I found it!"

She sounded happy. I wasn't. My bottle was supposed to
travel around the world.

"Julian?" Gloria said.

I didn't answer.

All that water to travel! All those countries to see! The
whole world full of strangers! And where did my stupid
bottle go? To Gloria's house!

"Julian?" Gloria said. "Are you still there?"

I couldn't talk. I was too disgusted. I hung up.

Gloria came looking for me.

"Tell her I'm not here," I said to Huey.

Huey went to the door. "Julian says he's not here," Huey said.

"Oh," Gloria said. She went away.

In a couple of days my father started noticing.

"I haven't seen Gloria lately," he said.

"I don't want to see her," I said.

"Why?" my father said.

"Because."

Then I decided to tell my father about the bottle and how Gloria found it. It didn't matter anymore to keep it a secret. The secret was over.

"That's too bad," my father said. "But it's not Gloria's fault."

"She found the bottle," I said. "She must be laughing at me for trying such a stupid idea."

"It's not a stupid idea," my father said. "You just had bad luck. You know what your problem is? It's the curve in the river. Your bottle got stuck on that curve, and it didn't have a chance."

I felt a little better. I went to see Gloria.

"I wanted to give you your bottle back," Gloria said. Then she added, "I thought it was a great idea, sending a message in a bottle."

"Well, it's a good idea, but it's a no-good idea because of the curve in the river. The bottle couldn't get around it," I explained.

"I guess it couldn't," Gloria said.

"Julian," my father said, "I have to make a long trip in the truck Saturday. I have to pick up some car parts. I'm going to go past the big bridge down the river. Would you like to ride along?"

I said I would.

"You know," my father said, "there's something we could do. We could walk out on the bridge. And if you wanted, you could send a new message. Your bottle would have a good chance from there. It's past the curve in the river."

I thought about it. I decided to do it. And I told my father.

"You know," he said, "if you don't mind my advice — put something special about yourself in the bottle, for the person who finds it."

"Why?" I asked.

"It'll give the wind and the water something special to carry. If you send something you care about, it might bring you luck."

I was working on my new message. And then I thought about Huey and Gloria. I thought how they might want to send bottles too. It didn't seem so important anymore that I be the only one to do it.

And that's what we did. We all got new bottles, and we put something special in each one. We each made a picture of ourselves for our bottle.

And in his, Huey put his favorite joke:

Where does a hamburger go on New Year's Eve?

To a meat ball.

In hers, Gloria put instructions on doing a cartwheel.

In mine, I wrote instructions for taking care of rabbits. . . .

We were ready for Saturday.

The bridge was long and silver and sparkled in the sun. It was so big that it looked like giants must have made it, that human beings never could have. But human beings did.

My father parked below the bridge. "From here we have to walk," he said.

We got out of the truck, which always smells a little bit of dust, but mostly of the raisins Dad keeps on the dashboard.

We walked in the outside walkers' lane to the middle of the river. Cars whizzed past. We each had our bottle in a backpack.

The bridge swayed a little. We could feel it vibrate. My father held Gloria's and Huey's hands. I held Gloria's other hand.

"It's scary, but it's safe," my father said.

We held on to the bridge railing and looked over the side. The green water slid under us very fast. For a minute it seemed like the bridge was moving and the water was standing still.

We unpacked our bottles.

"Don't just throw them over the side," my father said.
"Make some wishes. Sending messages around the world is
a big thing to do. Anytime you do a big thing, it's good to
make wishes."

We did.

I don't know what Huey or Gloria wished. I wished our
bottles would sail along together. I wished they wouldn't get
trapped in seaweed or ice, or hit rocks. I wished we'd make
new friends on the other side of the world. I wished we'd go
to meet them someday.

"Ready?" my father said.

Together we threw our bottles over the side. They made a
tiny splash. They looked very small, but we could see them
starting toward the ocean.

They were like Columbus's ships. I hoped they'd stay
together a long, long time.

Slippery Siblings

by Sandra Weber
photographs by Danny Bryant

Blaise Bryant and his sister, Joy, race bobsleds. When the Empire Games took place, they got the chance to compete. Blaise and Joy raced their bobsled down the course in less than thirty-seven seconds. They drove fast enough to win the gold medal!

· ·

"We were going like mean machines," says Blaise. "We were so fast that the catchers at the end of the track almost couldn't catch us." Blaise, who likes to be called "Hurricane," was the driver. He steered the sled through the icy corners at speeds up to 30 miles per hour. Not an easy task for any eight-year-old, but Blaise was born blind.

While Blaise drove the sled, Joy sat behind him. Her job this time was to keep her head tucked down and trust the driver. She would rather have been driving, but it was Blaise's turn.

This was Blaise's second year of bobsled racing and Joy's third year. They learned to ride at the youth bobsled program held at Mount Van Hoevenberg near Lake Placid, New York. Twice a week, they practice on the same frozen track used in the 1932 and 1980 Olympic Games.

The facility provides the special small-sized bobsleds. Riders must bring their own gear: a helmet, long pants, and heavy socks with sport boots.

It's the driver's job to get the sled down the quarter-mile track as fast as possible. You steer with ropes. But if you pull too hard, you will lose time on the curve. If you don't pull hard enough, you'll hit the top of the curve and maybe crash.

Joy and Blaise ride with other sledders during practice. Joy especially likes riding with other girls. But when it came time for the championship race, she teamed with her brother. Blaise says that Joy is his biggest helper on and off the track.

Why do they like bobsledding? Joy says, "I just like it. I like being with my friends." Blaise simply grins and says one word: "Speed."

During the warmer months, Joy and Blaise practice with their dad. He made a small run on a hill at the high school. They slide on a small sled with wheels. They also keep fit by jumping and flipping on their trampoline and swimming on the local team.

What is their next goal? To win even more gold medals at the Empire State Games.

Driving by the Numbers

Blaise loves math. He uses numbers, rather than his eyes, to drive the bobsled.

"My dad rode with me the first time down the track," says Blaise. "I counted while he told me when to turn right or left." That's all it took for Blaise to learn the course.

Now when the sled is pushed off, Blaise holds the sled's steering ropes and starts counting. He remembers the length of the straightaways and the steepness of the corners. And he feels the track curving.

If he senses the track going up on the left, he knows he has to turn right. He pulls lightly on the left rope to steer the bobsled through the curve.

When he wants to turn left, he pulls lightly on the right rope.

Think and Compare

1. Both *Slippery Siblings* and *A Curve in the River* tell about families spending time together. How are the family times the same and different?

2. Compare how Julian and Alex behave when things don't work out the way they want them to. What lessons do you think they learn?

3. If Blaise could give advice to the girl in *Thunder Cake*, what might he say about her fear of thunder?

4. Which character in this theme would you like to have for a friend? Why?

Strategies in Action Which reading strategies helped you the most in this theme? How did they help you?

Expressing

Write a Message

What if you found Julian's bottle with the message inside? Write a message back to him. Include something special about yourself.

Tips

- Be sure to include the date and your name.
- Include details that tell the reader about you.

Writing an Answer to a Question

Some tests ask you to write an answer to a question about something you have read. Here is a sample question for *A Curve in the River*.

Write your answer to this question.

What are two ways that Julian's father helped Julian?

1 **Understand the question.**

Find the key words in the question. Use them to understand what you need to do.

2 **Get ready to write.**

Look back at the selection. List the details that will help you answer the question.

Here is a sample planning chart.

Ways Julian's Father Helped
1 told him the bottle got stuck in the curve
2 brought kids to throw in their bottles

Write your answer.

Use details from your list. Write a complete answer.

Now read one student's answer.

Julian's father told Julian that the bottle got stuck in the curve in the river. That was why the bottle didn't go far. He brought Julian, Gloria, and Huey to the bridge so they could throw in their bottles past the curve.

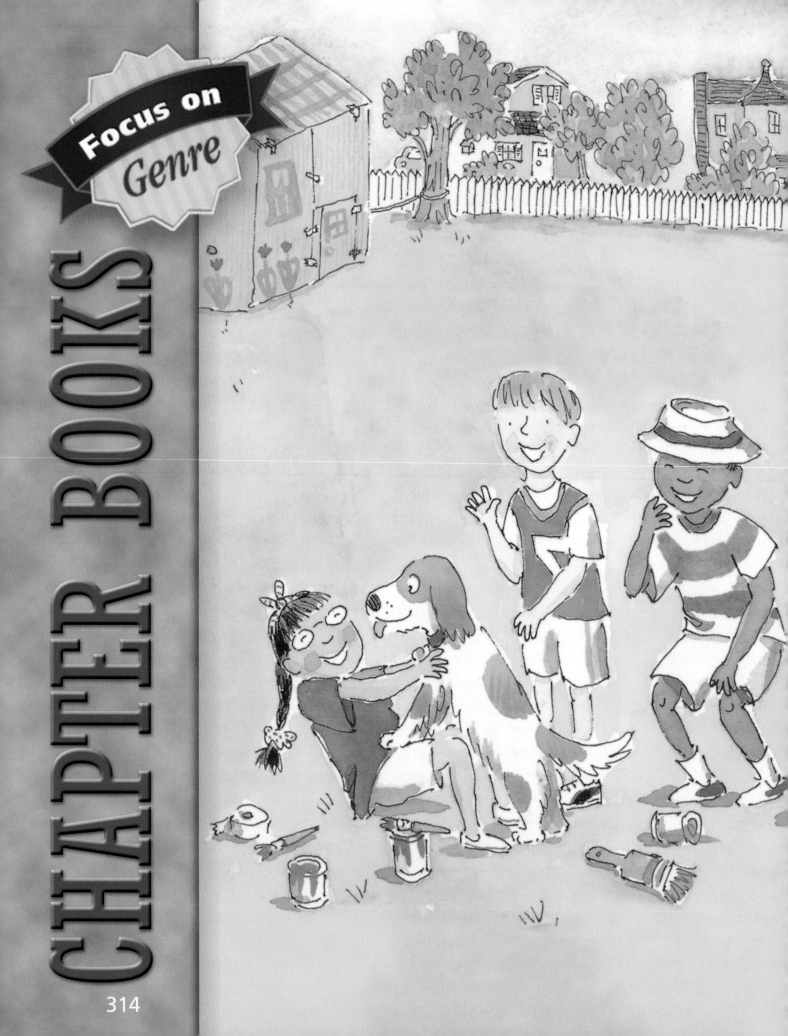

CHAPTER BOOKS

Chapter Books

Some stories take time to tell what happens.

A chapter book divides a story into parts, or **chapters**. The chapters may have titles or numbers. Each chapter tells a part of the story, often an exciting event.

As you read *The Cool Crazy Crickets* by David Elliot, see how the chapters work together to tell the story.

The Cool Crazy Crickets

by David Elliott
illustrated by Paul Meisel

Contents

Leo

Miranda

Noodles

Marcus

Phoebe

Chapter 1

The Club Gets a Name

It was a hot summer day. Leo and Marcus were sitting on Leo's front porch. They were swinging in a big wooden swing.

"Let's start a club," said Leo.

"Okay," said Marcus. "Who will be in it?"

"You and me," answered Leo.

"A two-person club?" said Marcus.

"Make that a four-person club," said Phoebe, as she and Miranda stepped onto the porch.

"We want to be in the club," said Phoebe. "Right, Miranda?"

"Right! If there is a club, we're in it," Miranda answered.

"Better let them in," Marcus said.

"Okay," Leo said. "You're in the club."

"Of course we are," Miranda said. "We already told you that."

"We are also in the swing," said Phoebe. "Move over."

"What's the name of the club?" asked Miranda. "A club should have a name."

"I have a good name for us," said Marcus. "The Doodles!"

"The Doodles?" said Miranda. "I don't want to be a Doodle."

"Neither do I," Phoebe said. "I want to be a Piñata. Let's name our club the Piñatas."

"People hit piñatas with big sticks," said Leo. "If we call ourselves the Piñatas, people might hit us."

Just then, from under the porch, a cricket began to sing. The cricket gave Phoebe an idea.

"That's it!" she shouted. "That's the name for us! The Crickets!"

"The Crickets?" Leo said. "If we name our club the Crickets, I'm quitting."

"Me, too," said Marcus. "We want a cool name for our club. Not some dumb name like the Crickets."

"How about the Cool Crickets, then?" said Phoebe.

"That's crazy," said Leo.

"How about the Cool *Crazy* Crickets, then?" said Miranda.

"The Cool Crazy Crickets," repeated Marcus.
"I like it!"

"Me, too," said Phoebe. "The Cool Crazy Crickets!"

Leo was silent. He looked at his friends.

Suddenly, he jumped high in the air.

"I'm cool!" he shouted. "I'm crazy! I'm a Cool
Crazy Cricket!"

And that's how the club got its name.

CHAPTER 2

The Club Gets a Clubhouse

It was the first meeting of the club. Leo was worried.

"We have a big problem," he said to the other Cool Crazy Crickets. "We have a club, but we don't have a clubhouse. Every club needs a clubhouse."

"That's not a problem," said Phoebe. "We can use my room."

The Cool Crazy Crickets ran to Phoebe's house.

They ran in the door.

They ran down the hall.

When they got to Phoebe's room, they stopped running.

"Come on in, Crickets!" Phoebe called.

"What's that on the window sill?" asked Miranda.

"Spaghetti!" Phoebe answered. "It's only two days old."

"Let's go to my room," said Marcus.

"Good idea," said Leo.

The Cool Crazy Crickets ran to Marcus's house.

Marcus's room was very nice.

It wasn't at all like Phoebe's.

It also wasn't empty.

"Oh no!" Miranda said.

"O NO!" yelled the little boy in Marcus's room.

"It's your little brother, Teddy!" said Leo.

"ME TEDDY!" Teddy yelled. "ME BRUDDER!"

Teddy was little, but Teddy was loud.

"Don't pay any attention to him," said Marcus. "He's just a baby."

"JUT BAY BEE!" yelled Teddy.

"Does he ever stop yelling?" asked Phoebe.

"When he's sleeping," said Marcus.

"WEN SWEE PING!" yelled Teddy.

"Yow!" said Leo. "Let's get out of here."

"OW DA HEER!" Teddy yelled.

The Crickets ran back to Leo's yard.

"Finding a clubhouse isn't going to be easy," said Miranda.

Just then, a big truck stopped in front of Leo's house. Two men got out of the truck.

"Is this 52 Prince Street?" asked the driver.

"Yes," said Leo.

"Well, your new refrigerator is here," said the man.

The Cool Crazy Crickets watched as the men moved a big box off the truck.

"Wow!" said Marcus. "That box is almost as big as a house!"

"Hey, it could be our clubhouse!" cried Leo.

"It's kind of small for four people," said Phoebe.

"We have another empty box in the truck," said the driver. "You can have that one, too."

For the next two hours, the Cool Crazy Crickets were very busy, cutting and taping and painting.

Leo made a secret entrance and a special door for Noodles.

Phoebe made a peephole.

Miranda made the clubhouse beautiful.

Marcus made a booby trap to keep out spies. Even Noodles helped.

Finally, the clubhouse was finished.

"It's fantastic!" said Leo.

"It's stupendous!" said Phoebe.

"It's incredible!" said Miranda.

"It's ours!" said Marcus.

The Cool Crazy Crickets went inside.

Leo began to laugh.

"Do you know why this is the perfect clubhouse for us?" he asked.

"Why?" asked the other Crickets.

"Well, this is a *refrigerator* box, isn't it?" asked Leo.

"Yes," said Phoebe. "So?"

"So," said Leo, "we are the *Cool* Crazy Crickets, aren't we?"

CHAPTER 3
The Club Gets a Mascot

The next day, Marcus, Phoebe, and Miranda were sitting in their new clubhouse. Leo came in through the secret entrance.

"Where were you?" asked Marcus. "We've been waiting for you."

"I had to take care of Noodles," said Leo. "I had to feed him and give him water and take him for a walk."

"I've called this meeting of the club," said Leo, "because we have another problem."

"What is it this time?" asked Miranda. "What's the new problem?"

"We need a mascot," said Leo. "Every club should have a mascot."

"A mask? Why do we need a mask?" asked Marcus.
"Is this some kind of Halloween club?"

"Let's call ourselves the Trick or Treaters!" said Phoebe.

"Not a mask," said Leo. "A *mascot*."

"Yes, we need a mascot!" said Phoebe. "Uh, what's
a mascot?"

"A mascot brings good luck," Leo said. "It's usually
some kind of animal."

Suddenly, Noodles sat up.

He was an animal.

He could be a mascot!

Noodles looked straight at Miranda.

"I have it!" she said. "I know the perfect mascot!"

"Let's guess who it is," said Leo.

"Okay," said Miranda. "Here's a clue. He is very beautiful."

Noodles cocked his ears. He gazed at Phoebe with his big, brown, beautiful eyes.

"I know who it is!" Phoebe shouted. "And Miranda is right. He is the perfect mascot for us."

"Don't tell us yet," said Leo. "Give us another clue."

"Okay," said Phoebe. "He is also very friendly."
Noodles wagged his tail and licked Marcus's face.

"I know who it is!" Marcus shouted. "He is also very smart. Right?"

"Right!" answered Phoebe and Miranda.

Noodles rolled over. He stood up on his hind legs. He stood up on his front legs. He did the smartest tricks he knew.

"I give up," said Leo. "Who is the perfect mascot?"

Noodles moved to the center of the clubhouse floor. What a fine mascot he would make!

"It's my goldfish, Finny," shouted Marcus.

"It's not Finny," shouted Miranda. "It's my cat, Ralph!"

"It's not Ralph," shouted Phoebe. "It's my parakeet, Mr. Pete!"

Poor Noodles. He wasn't a goldfish or a cat or a parakeet. He was just a shaggy little dog.

Suddenly, the clubhouse was filled with a delicious smell. A plate of warm chocolate chip cookies came through the window.

"These are for taking such good care of Noodles this morning," said Leo's dad.

Leo put the plate in the middle of the clubhouse floor. Each of the Crickets took a cookie. For a moment, the clubhouse was quiet.

"That's it!" Leo suddenly shouted.

"What?" asked Miranda.

"A mascot brings good luck, right?" asked Leo.

"So?" said Marcus.

"What about Noodles?" said Leo. "He brought us good luck."

"That's right!" said Miranda. "If it hadn't been for Noodles, we wouldn't be eating these cookies right now."

"Let's take a vote," said Phoebe. "Whoever thinks that Noodles should be our mascot, put your hand up."

Four hands shot up in the air.

"Hooray for Noodles!" the Crickets shouted.

How proud Noodles was! He had walked into the clubhouse that morning just a shaggy little dog.

But he walked out a mascot!

CHAPTER 4

But What Kind of Club Is It?

Marcus and Miranda were walking over to Leo's house for the third meeting of the club.

"There is one thing I don't understand about our club," said Marcus.

"What's that?" asked Miranda.

"We have a name for our club, right?" said Marcus.

"Right," said Miranda.

"And we have a clubhouse and a mascot, right?"

"Right," said Miranda. "So what is the problem?"

"The problem is," said Marcus, "we don't know what kind of club it is."

"Hey, you're right!" said Miranda.

Just then, Miranda saw Phoebe and Leo coming up the street.

"Hey," she called, "We have a problem! We're in a club . . ."

"But we don't know what kind of club we're in," finished Marcus.

"Oh, no!" said Phoebe. "Another problem."

"Let's go into the clubhouse to decide," said Leo.

"Let's take a vote on what kind of club it should be," said Miranda.

"I say it should be a snack club," said Marcus.

"What's a snack club?" asked Phoebe.

"Well, you just bring a bunch of snacks and then you eat them," said Marcus.

"That's dumb," said Phoebe.

"Plus, we don't want ants in our clubhouse," said Miranda.

"How about a joke club?" said Phoebe.

"Okay," said Miranda. "Someone tell a joke."

"I'll go first," said Marcus. "Why did Leo put the mascot in the refrigerator?"

"Why?" asked Miranda, Leo, and Phoebe.

"Because he wanted a dish of cold noodles. Get it? Noodles is our mascot and . . ."

"Maybe a joke club isn't such a good idea," said Leo.

"I know!" said Miranda. "How about a traveling club?"

"What's a traveling club?" Leo asked.

"You travel to different places and then you write reports about them."

"That's not a traveling club!" said Marcus. "That's a homework club!"

"I'm not going to be in any club that has homework," said Phoebe.

"Okay," said Miranda. "We're not in a traveling club."

"And we're not in a joke club," said Phoebe.

"And we're not in a snack club," said Marcus.

"So what kind of club are we in?" Leo asked.

The clubhouse was silent.

"That does it!" said Marcus. "I'm quitting."

"Me, too," Phoebe said. "I'm not going to be in a club if I don't know what kind of club it is."

For a moment, it seemed that it was the end of the Cool Crazy Crickets.

"Wait!" said Leo, as his friends were crawling out the door. "I know what kind of club it is!"

"You do?" Miranda asked.

"Sure," said Leo. "It's an F. F. L. club!"

"A what?" asked Marcus.

"An F. F. L. club," Leo repeated.

"What does F. F. L. mean?" asked Phoebe. "Four Funny La-dee-das?"

"No," said Leo. "Friends For Life."

"A Friends For Life club?" Marcus said. "That's crazy."

"Right!" Leo said. "But don't forget. We are the Cool *Crazy* Crickets!"

"Look!" Marcus shouted. "I'm a Cricket! I'm a Cool Crazy Cricket!"

"Me, too!" said Miranda.

"Me, three!" said Phoebe.

"Me, four!" said Leo.

"Arf! Arf!" barked Noodles.

And, of course, that's exactly who they were.

Four friends and a mascot.

The Cool Crazy Crickets! Friends For Life!

THE END

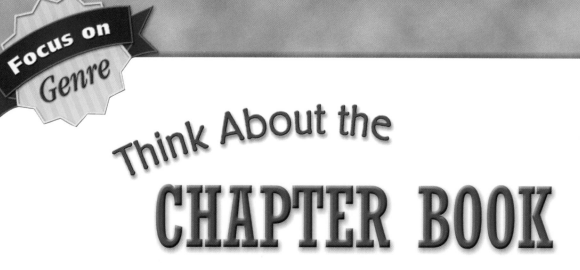
Think About the CHAPTER BOOK

1. Look back at the chapter titles. Why do you think the author uses chapters to tell this story?

2. Why do you think Leo wanted to start a club?

3. Is a Friends for Life Club a good kind of club for the Cool Crazy Crickets? Explain.

4. Which chapter is your favorite? Why?

Internet

Post a Review

Would you recommend the book *The Cool Crazy Crickets* to someone? Why or why not? Post a review on Education Place. **www.eduplace.com/kids**

Creating

Write a Chapter

The Cool Crazy Crickets are ready for another adventure. Think about what might happen next to the four friends. Then use this event to write a new chapter for the story. You can add a new character or put the friends in a new setting. Make sure to give the characters a problem to solve in your chapter.

Tips

- **Think about what has already happened in the story.**
- **Make sure that the event makes sense with the rest of the story.**
- **Write a catchy title for your chapter.**

Theme **6**

Talent Show

My music

reaches

to the sky.

Chippewa proverb

Talent Show

with Tomie dePaola

Can a person be good at more than one thing? Tomie dePaola thinks so. He has many talents! Today he wants to share his ideas about talent with you.

346

Dear Friends,

I remember the first talent show I was ever in. It was called The Playground Follies. It was a talent show put on by kids from all the different summer playgrounds in Meriden, Connecticut, where I lived.

I sang, "Casey would waltz with the strawberry blonde and the band played on" to a little red-haired girl. Then we waltzed around the stage. Lots of kids did lots of things, like singing, dancing, acrobatics, all kinds of stuff like that.

There were lots of talent shows when I was growing up. But they all had to do with performing.

I think there can be a different kind of talent show! You could have it right in your classroom, and it wouldn't have to be just singing and dancing. For example, if you are a good artist you could put up some artwork. If you like to read, you could read a story or something else interesting to the class. If you like a sport, you could give a little demonstration on how to do it. There are lots of things you could do.

Everyone in your class has some kind of TALENT, and I bet that each talent is different! What a great thing to share. That's the kind of talent show I'd like to see.

Now what could I do? Sing? Dance? Draw? How about you?

All the best,

Jamie

P. S. My talents make me happy, and I enjoy sharing them with others. I hope your talents make you happy, too. They are part of what makes you special! Thanks for letting me share my ideas with you. Now I hope you enjoy reading about all the talented people in this theme.

See a Talent Show

Tomie dePaola has lots of ideas about how to share talents with others. If you were in a talent show, what talent would you like to share?

You are about to read some selections about talented characters. You will find out how they discover their talents, and how they get better and better at what they do. As you read, compare how the characters feel about their special talents. Enjoy the talent show!

Internet

To learn about the authors in this theme, visit Education Place. **www.eduplace.com/kids**

The Art Lesson

Genre **Realistic Fiction**

Key Vocabulary

chalk
copy
crayons
powders
practice
smock

Vocabulary Reader

MAKING PICTURES
by Kristin Cashore

e • Glossary

Be an Artist

The Art Lesson is the story of a boy who wants to be an artist when he grows up. What would you need to be an artist? It depends on what kind of art you want to make.

Crayons are great for making brightly colored drawings.

Many artists like to draw with **chalk**.

Some paints are made by adding water to colored **powders**.

Art students
sometimes **copy**
famous paintings
or illustrations.
It takes a lot
of **practice**
to become a
good artist.

When you paint,
it's a good idea
to wear a **smock**
to protect
your clothes!

The Art Lesson

Tomie dePaola

Strategy Focus

As you read about a boy who loves to draw pictures, **evaluate** the way the author uses words and pictures to tell the story.

Tommy knew he wanted to be an artist
when he grew up. He drew pictures
everywhere he went. It was his favorite thing
to do.

His friends had favorite things to do, too. Jack collected all kinds of turtles. Herbie made huge cities in his sandbox. Jeannie, Tommy's best friend, could do cartwheels and stand on her head.

But Tommy drew and drew and drew.

His twin cousins, who were already
grown up, were in art school learning to be
real artists. They told him not to copy and
to practice, practice, practice. So, he did.

Tommy put his pictures up on the walls
of his half of the bedroom.

His mom put them up all around the house.

His dad took them to the barber shop
where he worked.

Tom and Nana, Tommy's Irish grandfather
and grandmother, had his pictures in their
grocery store.

Nana-Fall-River, his Italian grandmother,
put one in a special frame on the table next
to the photograph of Aunt Clo in her
wedding dress.

Once Tommy took a flashlight and a pencil under the covers and drew pictures on his sheets. But when his mom changed the sheets on Monday and found them, she said, "No more drawing on the sheets, Tommy."

His mom and dad were having a new house built, so Tommy drew pictures of what it would look like when it was finished.

When the walls were up, one of the carpenters gave Tommy a piece of bright blue chalk. Tommy took the chalk and drew beautiful pictures all over the unfinished walls.

But, when the painters came, his dad said, "That's it, Tommy. No more drawing on the walls."

Tommy couldn't wait to go to kindergarten.
His brother, Joe, told him there was a real art
teacher who came to the school to give
ART LESSONS!

"When do we have our art lessons?"
Tommy asked the kindergarten teacher.

"Oh, you won't have your art lessons until
next year," said Miss Bird. "But, we are going
to paint pictures tomorrow."

It wasn't much fun.

The paint was awful and the paper got all wrinkly. Miss Bird made the paint by pouring different colored powders into different jars and mixing them with water. The paint didn't stick to the paper very well and it cracked.

If it was windy when Tommy carried his picture home, the paint blew right off the paper.

"At least you get more than one piece of paper in kindergarten," his brother, Joe, said. "When the art teacher comes, you only get one piece."

Tommy knew that the art teacher came to the school every other Wednesday. He could tell she was an artist because she wore a blue smock over her dress and she always carried a big box of thick colored chalks.

Once, Tommy and Jeannie looked at the
drawings that were hung up in the hallway.
They were done by the first graders.

"Your pictures are much better," Jeannie
told Tommy. "Next year when we have real art
lessons, you'll be the best one!"

Tommy could hardly wait. He practiced all
summer. Then, on his birthday, which was right
after school began, his mom and dad gave him a
box of sixty-four Crayola crayons. Regular boxes
of crayons had red, orange, yellow, green, blue,
violet, brown and black. This box had so many
other colors: blue-violet, turquoise, red-orange,
pink and even gold, silver and copper.

"Class," said Miss Landers, the first-grade teacher, "next month, the art teacher will come to our room, so on Monday instead of Singing, we will practice using our crayons."

On Monday, Tommy brought his sixty-four
crayons to school. Miss Landers was not
pleased. "Everyone must use the same
crayons," she said.

"SCHOOL CRAYONS!"

School crayons had only the same old
eight colors. As Miss Landers passed them
out to the class, she said, "These crayons are
school property, so do not break them, peel off
the paper, or wear down the points."

"How am I supposed to practice being an artist with SCHOOL CRAYONS?" Tommy asked Jack and Herbie.

"That's enough, Tommy," Miss Landers said. "And I want you to take those birthday crayons home with you and leave them there."

And Joe was right. They only got ONE piece of paper.

Finally, the day of the art lesson came. Tommy could hardly sleep that night.

The next morning, he hid the box of sixty-four crayons under his sweater and went off to school. He was ready!

The classroom door opened and in walked the art teacher. Miss Landers said, "Class, this is Mrs. Bowers, the art teacher. Patty, who is our paper monitor this week, will give out one piece of paper to each of you. And remember, don't ruin it because it is the only piece you'll get. Now, pay attention to Mrs. Bowers."

"Class," Mrs. Bowers began, "because Thanksgiving is not too far away, we will learn to draw a Pilgrim man, a Pilgrim woman and a turkey. Watch carefully and copy me."

Copy? COPY? Tommy knew that real artists didn't copy.

This was terrible. This was supposed to be a real art lesson. He folded his arms and just sat there. "Now what's the matter?" Miss Landers asked. Tommy looked past her and spoke right to Mrs. Bowers.

"I'm going to be an artist when I grow up and my cousins told me that real artists don't copy. And besides, Miss Landers won't let me use my own sixty-four Crayola crayons."

"Well, well," Mrs. Bowers said. "What are we going to do?" She turned to Miss Landers and they whispered together. Miss Landers nodded.

"Now, Tommy," Mrs. Bowers said. "It wouldn't be fair to let you do something different from the rest of the class.

"But, I have an idea. If you draw the
Pilgrim man and woman and the turkey, and if
there's any time left, I'll give you another piece
of paper and you can do your own picture with
your own crayons. Can you do that?"

"I'll try," Tommy said, with a big smile.

And he did.

And he did.

And he still does.

Meet the Author and Illustrator

Tomie dePaola

Other Books

The Baby Sister

The Legend of the Indian Paintbrush

26 Fairmont Avenue

Fact File

- Tomie dePaola's name is pronounced like this: Tommy da-POW-la

- He grew up in Meriden, Connecticut, and many of his stories are about his childhood there. He based the story of *The Art Lesson* on his own life.

- When he was a child, some of his favorite things to do were drawing, painting, writing poetry, and tap-dancing.

- He uses tempera, watercolor, and acrylic paints for his illustrations.

Internet

Tomie dePaola wrote *The Art Lesson* for his favorite art teacher, the real Mrs. Beulah Bowers. To find out about the true story behind *The Art Lesson,* visit Education Place.

www.eduplace.com/kids

Think About the Selection

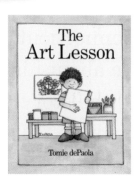

The Art Lesson
Tomie dePaola

1. Why do you think Tomie dePaola wrote this story?

2. Tommy's cousins told him not to copy. What do you think of their advice?

3. Why do you think Tommy decided to take his birthday crayons back to school?

4. What do you think Miss Landers and Mrs. Bowers were whispering about?

5. **Connecting/Comparing** How did some of the other characters in the story feel about Tommy's talent for drawing?

Informing

Write an Invitation

Write an invitation to an art show at your school. Tell a friend all about your art show.

Tips

- Tell where and when the show will take place.
- Use adjectives to make the show sound interesting.

Art

Draw a Job

Make a list of five things that you like to do. Then choose one that you could do as a job when you grow up. Draw a picture of yourself doing that job.

Listening and Speaking

Role-Play a Conversation

With a partner, role-play a conversation between Tommy and one of his teachers. Use your voice to show how each character is feeling.

Internet

Take an Online Poll

Is art your favorite subject in school? Do you want to be an artist when you grow up? What is your favorite book by Tomie dePaola? Take our online poll to tell us.

www.eduplace.com/kids

Carmen Lomas Garza

Look carefully at the painting on the right. You see a family working together in a kitchen. You may have noticed the bright colors and patterns. Did you also see the keys hanging on the wall?

Look again. You probably noticed something else that you didn't see the first time you looked. The picture you are looking at was painted by Carmen Lomas Garza. Carmen's paintings are so full of interesting details that you can look at them over and over again, and always find something new.

Tamalada (Making Tamales), 1987

Carmen taught herself to draw by practicing every day. She would draw whatever was in front of her — books, cats, her left hand, her sisters and brothers, paper bags, flowers. Carmen drew anything or anybody that would stay still for a few minutes.

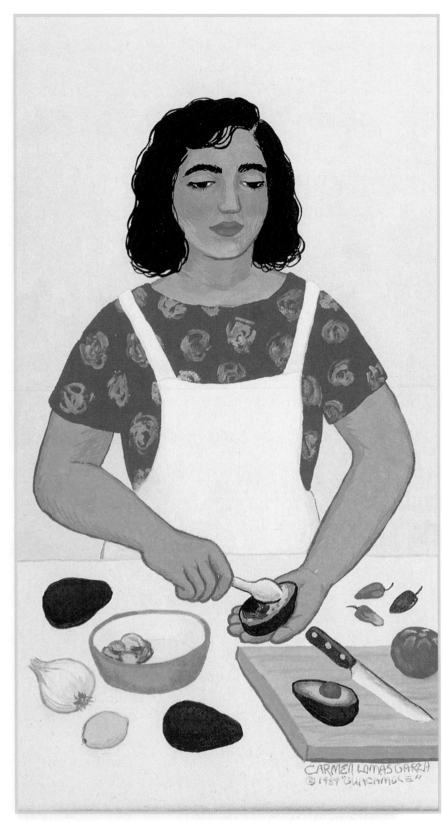

Guacamole, 1989

One painting may be a picture of people dancing at a party. Another may show Carmen and members of her family picking fruit, celebrating a birthday, or just getting together to cook food. Sometimes, she even includes the family cat, or a lizard she might have seen crawling on the porch.

Naranjas (Oranges), 1990

Carmen's work has been shown in museums all around the country. She has also written popular books for children. Carmen hopes that her paintings and books will help people learn more about her Mexican-American culture.

Instructions

The purpose of writing instructions is to tell others how to do or make something. Use this student's writing as a model when you write instructions of your own.

> The **title** tells what the instructions are about.

> Sometimes it is good to **introduce** your instructions topic.

How to Snorkel

If you like to swim and see an interesting underwater world, then you might want to try snorkeling. It is fun to snorkel anywhere. You can snorkel in your bathtub, a swimming pool, or a lake. Snorkeling is a nature sport where you wear a clear mask and a special underwater breathing device called a snorkel.

To snorkel, you need a snorkel, mask, and fins. The first step is to slide the mask securely over your forehead and nose. Next, put the mouthpiece in your mouth. Make sure the snorkel tube is above your head so when you swim the snorkel is above the surface of the water. Then put your fins on your feet.

Finally, start swimming on your belly, and breathe through the snorkel tube. Now it is time for the fun part. Look for the amazing underwater world. You may see plants, rocks, fish, someone's feet, or even your bathtub drain!

Good instructions tell what to do in a clear **order**.

Use **time-order words** to show the reader what to do first, next, and last.

Meet the Author

Bryan O.

Grade: two

State: California

Hobbies: reading nonfiction books, collecting sports cards, and swimming

What he'd like to be when he grows up: a scientist or a pastor

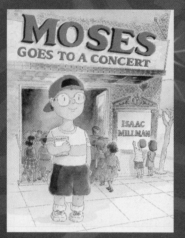

Moses Goes to a Concert

Genre **Realistic Fiction**

Key Vocabulary

deaf

hearing

instruments

sign

vibrations

Vocabulary Reader

Let's All Dance

e • Glossary

Communicating with Sign Language

A person who is **deaf** is someone who is either partly or completely unable to hear. In the story you are about to read, a deaf boy and his classmates go to a concert.

How does a person without the sense of **hearing** enjoy music or talk to someone? Deaf people are able to make music a part of their lives because they can feel the **vibrations** that certain **instruments**, such as drums or tubas, make.

To communicate with other people, a person who is deaf may **sign** the things he or she wants to say. Signing is a type of language made up of hand movements.

In the story *Moses Goes to a Concert*, the character named Marjorie Elwyn is based on this real-life musician, Evelyn Glennie.

Manual Alphabet

Meet the Author and Illustrator
Isaac Millman

Isaac Millman started writing because it made the stories he drew seem more alive. He says that writing, to him, is "drawing with words." He takes his stories from things he sees around him.

Mr. Millman and his wife live in New York City. They have been married forty years and have two grown sons and a grandson. *Moses Goes to a Concert* is Mr. Millman's first book, but he plans to write many more.

Another Book Illustrated by Isaac Millman:
Howie Bowles, Secret Agent

Internet

To find out more about Isaac Millman, visit Education Place. **www.eduplace.com/kids**

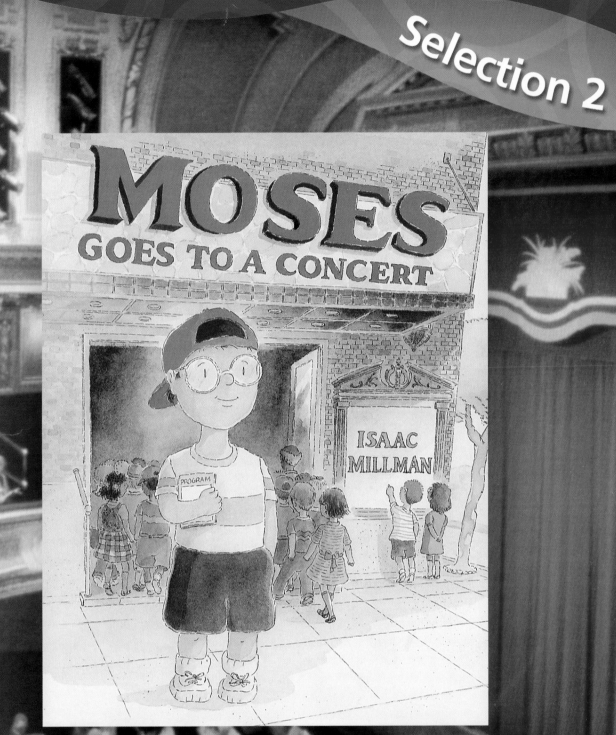

MOSES
GOES TO A CONCERT

ISAAC MILLMAN

A boy who is deaf goes to a concert with his classmates. As you read, stop to **summarize** the important facts in the story.

Moses plays on his new drum.

He can't hear the sounds he is making because he is deaf, but he feels the vibration of the drum through his hands. He has taken off his shoes so he can feel it through his feet, too.

| I | PLAY | THE DRUM |

Today, Moses is going on a field trip. His
teacher, Mr. Samuels, is taking him and his
classmates, who are all deaf, to a young
people's concert.

As the children climb onto the bus, they wonder
what is inside Mr. Samuels's black bag.

"A big surprise," signs Mr. Samuels.

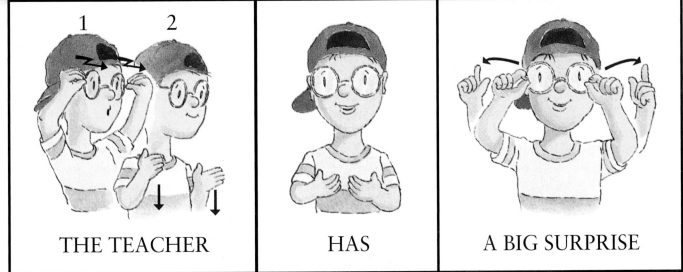

THE TEACHER HAS A BIG SURPRISE

On the bus, Moses signs to his friend. "John!
My parents gave me a new drum!"
John signs back. "I got one, too!"

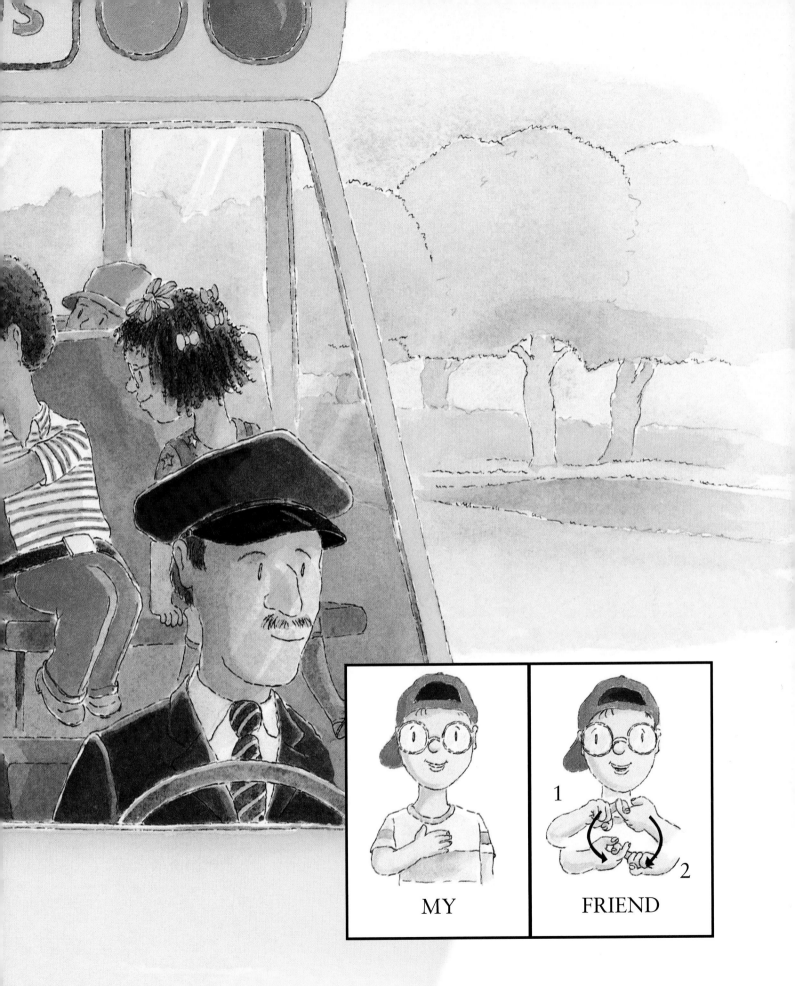

MY

FRIEND

Children from all over the city are coming to the concert. Moses and his friend John wait for their class to get off the bus so they can go inside together.

398

399

Mr. Samuels leads them to their seats in the first row. Across the stage, in front of the orchestra, are all the percussion instruments.

"Children, the percussionist is a friend of mine," signs Mr. Samuels.

1
2
A LOUD

MUSICAL

SOUND

401

"What's a percussionist?" Anna signs back.

"A musician who plays an instrument such as a drum, cymbals, even a piano," replies Mr. Samuels.

A young woman walks onto the stage. Everyone stands up to applaud. Some of Moses's classmates wave instead of clapping. The percussionist smiles and bows to the audience.

WE WAVE AND APPLAUD

"She has no shoes!" Moses signs in surprise.

The teacher smiles and signs, "She is deaf, too. She follows the orchestra by feeling the vibrations of the music through her stocking feet."

Then Mr. Samuels takes eleven balloons out of his black bag and hands one to each of his students.

"Oh! What beautiful balloons!"
Anna signs.

"Hold them on your laps," signs Mr.
Samuels. "They'll help you feel the music."

ELEVEN   BEAUTIFUL   BALLOONS

The conductor turns to face the orchestra and raises his baton. The percussionist strikes the huge gong and the concert begins.

The percussionist watches the conductor and moves from one instrument to the next, striking each to make a sound. Moses and his classmates hold their balloons in their laps. They can feel the music as their balloons pick up the vibrations.

I   FEEL   VIBRATIONS

When the concert is over, Mr. Samuels has another
surprise. He takes the children onstage to meet his
friend, Ms. Marjorie Elwyn. "She will tell you how she
became a percussionist," signs Mr. Samuels.

| [MY] FRIENDS | AND | I | ARE DEAF |

"I became seriously ill at the age of seven," signs
Ms. Elwyn. "And when I recovered, I found out that
I had lost my hearing. I was deaf."

"What did you do then?" signs Moses.

I   WORKED HARD.

MY

HEART

WAS SET ON

BECOMING

A PERCUSSIONIST

AND

I

DID.

413

"Now you can play on my musical instruments,"
Ms. Elwyn signs. "Come with me, children."

Ann plays on the marimba . . .
Beverly strikes the triangle . . .

Mark pounds the floor tom and the cymbal . . .
Dianne beats the tom-toms . . . John hits the snare
drum . . . and Moses thumps the bass drum . . .

David strikes the gong . . . Tommy and Suzy play
on the tubular bells . . . while Steve bangs the
kettledrum and Maria plays the congas.

"Children! We have to go!" Mr. Samuels
announces after a while. "Ms. Elwyn has to get
ready for another concert."

Moses and his classmates sign
thank you, and they wave goodbye
to Ms. Elwyn.

THANKS

GOODBYE

417

On the bus on the way home, Moses signs, "It was so much fun!"

SO MUCH

FUN

That night, Moses tells his parents about the concert. Here is what he says:

WHEN   YOU

SET YOUR MIND TO IT,

YOU

CAN

BECOME

ANYTHING

YOU

WANT

WHEN

YOU

GROW UP . . .

421

A DOCTOR,

ARTIST,

TEACHER,

LAWYER,

FARMER,

ELECTRICIAN,

OR

ACTOR.

I

WANT

TO BECOME

A PERCUSSIONIST.

Responding

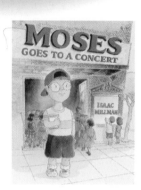

Think About the Selection

1. Why do you think Ms. Elwyn shares her experiences with Moses' class?

2. Which details helped you understand how Moses and his classmates were able to enjoy the concert?

3. What does Moses mean when he says, "When you set your mind to it, you can become anything you want . . ."?

4. Think of a concert you have gone to or music you have heard. How is your experience the same as Moses'? How is it different?

5. **Connecting/Comparing** Compare Mr. Samuels to the teachers in *The Art Lesson*.

Expressing

Write a Review

Think of a concert you have attended or some music that you like. Write a review that gives your opinion.

Tips

- Include the title of the piece of music and the name of the performer.
- Explain why you liked or disliked the music or concert.

Experiment with Sounds

Stretch a rubber band over a cup's opening. Gently pluck the rubber band, then squeeze the cup gently to change its shape. Pluck the rubber band again. When you change the cup's shape, how does the sound change?

Sign Your Name

Study the hand alphabet on page 389. Practice spelling your name. Then sign the letters of your name to a partner.

Bonus Sign your partner's name.

Internet

E-mail a Friend

What did you like about *Moses Goes to a Concert*? Is there anything you didn't like? Send an e-mail to a friend. Tell him or her about the story.

www.eduplace.com/kids

Genre

Concert Programs

Skill: How to Read a Concert Program

When you read a concert program, look for the following information:

- The title of the concert, and the date and time are usually listed first.

- The **performers** are the singers or musicians onstage.

- The **composer** wrote the music or words.

Go to a Concert

by Avery Hart and Paul Mantell

If you've never been to a concert, are you ever in for a treat! A concert is a chance to hear musicians playing the music they know best.

You can find out about what concerts are coming up in the area by checking the entertainment section of the newspaper. Free concerts are usually advertised on library bulletin boards. There are usually a lot of free concerts in the summer when they can be held in parks, and also at holiday time, when schools and community orchestras like to perform. Ask a grown-up to take you to one.

North Elementary School Spring Recital

May 21, 7:30 p.m.
Directed by: Mr. Dawe

Green Speckled Frogs

by Raffi — Performed by Ms. Cronin's first grade class

Swallowed a Fly

by Alan Mills — Performed by Mr. Lim's second grade class

Erie Canal

by Thomas S. Allen — Performed by Mrs. Serpa's third grade class

Be sure to arrive early enough to get a good seat, in case there is open seating, which is first come, first served. During the performance, sit back, turn on your imagination, and enjoy. The only rule is "No Talking, Please" — at a concert, it's the musicians who get to make the noise!

At folk and rock concerts, you can show your appreciation by clapping along with the music. At a classical concert, save your reaction for the end — even if the musicians take occasional pauses during their performances. But at the end of a classical concert, clap as hard as you wish. You can even stand up and shout "Bravo!" if you think the music was absolutely wonderful.

Background and Vocabulary

The School Mural

Genre Realistic Fiction

Key Vocabulary

event
mural
pride
project
scene
sketches

Vocabulary Reader

Making a MURAL
by Debbie O'Brien

e ● Glossary

A Mural

A **mural** is a large painting done on a wall or sometimes on a ceiling. Making a mural can be a big **event**. **Sketches**, or plans for the painting, have to be made before painting can begin.

In some cases, a team of people will work together to create a mural. Working on a big **project** like a mural can be more than fun. It can also be a way for people to show their **pride**, especially if the mural shows a **scene** that is important to the community where it is painted.

In the story you are about to read, a group of schoolchildren makes a mural that shows just how they feel about their school.

The School Mural

Written by
Sarah Vázquez

Illustrated by
Melinda Levine

A group of schoolchildren work together to show their school pride. As you read the story, think of **questions** to ask about their experience.

1
The News

One morning, Mrs. Sanchez greeted her class. "I have some news. Soon our school will be fifty years old. We're going to have an open house on May twenty-fifth to celebrate this big event."

Mrs. Sanchez said, "Each class will make a big project. It should be about our school and our community."

Paul asked, "What should we do?"

"I'm sure you'll think of some good ideas," said Mrs. Sanchez.

The class went outside for recess. Mei Lee
(MAY-lee) and Paul raced for the swings. They liked
to see who could swing the highest.

Mei Lee thought about the big project. She said,
"I think we should write a song or put on a play for
our class project. What do you think?"

437

Mrs. Sanchez listed the children's ideas on the board. "These are all good ideas," said Mrs. Sanchez. "Let's pick one that everyone can have a part in. Look over the list again. Then we'll vote on our project."

Mrs. Sanchez pointed to each idea as they voted. At first, not many children voted. Then, she pointed to the mural idea. Sixteen children raised their hands!

"I think you picked a fine project that everyone can work on," said Mrs. Sanchez.

banner
bookmarks
card
mural
song
play

3
The Plan

Mrs. Sanchez said, "People from many different cultures have painted on walls. Long ago, cave people painted on the walls of their caves. Their paintings tell us how people lived then. Here is a picture of a cave painting. It is a kind of mural." She held up the picture.

"Murals are huge! We'll need to think of lots of things to show," said Maria.

Mrs. Sanchez said, "Murals tell about people and their community. Think of some things to tell about your school."

"Let's tell people about our school band," said Beto.

"We'll need a really big wall for our mural," said Maria.

"What about the outside wall we see when we swing on the playground?" said Paul. "All the classes see it every day!"

Mrs. Sanchez said, "I'll ask our principal, Mr. Ford, if it's OK. Mei Lee, since the mural was your idea, please go with me to see him."

Later, Mrs. Sanchez said, "The principal likes the idea of painting a mural on the wall. He said he will ask if the local newspaper will take a picture of the mural. That would show how our community works together."

Beto asked, "Where will we get the paint? We'll need lots of brushes, too."

Paul said, "Let's ask the art teacher for help. Maybe we could ask our families to help us, too. My mom loves to paint."

"Good idea. Please tell your families about our project, and then I'll call them," said Mrs. Sanchez.

4
Painting the Mural

For the next three weeks, the class worked on the mural. First, they planned the scenes to draw. Next, the art teacher helped the children draw sketches of the different scenes on the wall.

Then they started painting the mural. Twenty children couldn't all paint at once, so they took turns. First the band group painted. Then the next group painted. Some parents helped paint the high parts of the wall near the roof. It was hard work, but everyone had fun.

Some funny things happened. One day, Paul bumped the paint tray and got paint all over himself. Then he slipped and put his hands on the wall. He left his handprints on the mural! Everyone decided it looked good, so they added their handprints, too.

Another time, Anjelina was painting high up on a ladder. She dipped the brush into the bucket and splattered lots of paint onto the wall. But down below her was Beto, so she splattered him, too! He had green hair that day.

5
The Newspaper

When the mural was finished, Mr. Ford called the newspaper. A reporter came to write a story. He asked the class many questions about how they made the mural. He got everyone's name. He took photos of the mural with the painters in front of it. He told the children to watch for the article soon.

The children could hardly wait to see the article in the newspaper. After about a week, the article appeared with a big photo of the mural. The headline said, "Children Show School Pride."

6
The Open House

On the day of the open house, Mr. Ford spoke to all the children, parents, and visitors. He told everyone what project each class had done. Then he invited the visitors to walk around and see all the projects. The children were very proud and excited.

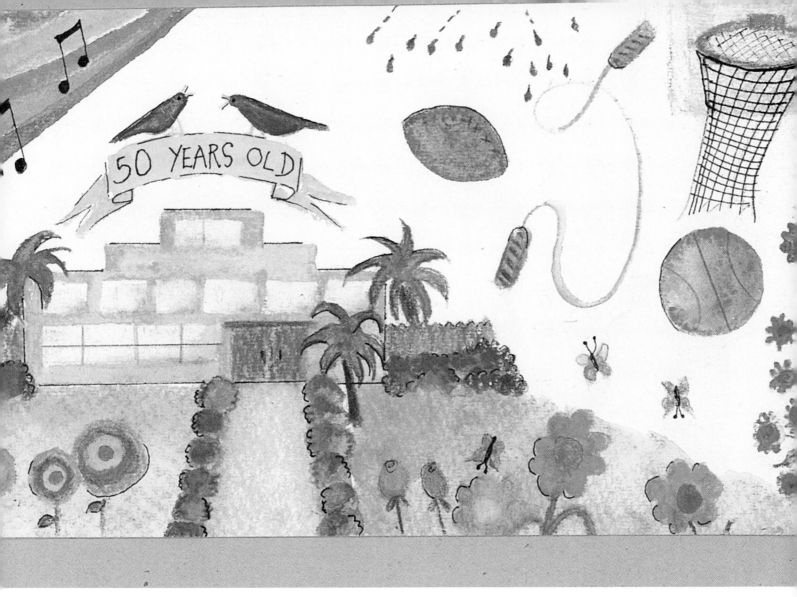

When Mr. Ford told about the mural, the crowd cheered. One neighbor stood up and thanked the students for making such a beautiful painting. He said people would enjoy it for many years.

The newspaper reporter came again, too. He took pictures of the mural and the children.

Some of the children decided they liked painting so much that it became their new hobby. Someday they might be famous painters. Or maybe they'll come back to the school sometime just to enjoy their mural. They might even tell students the story of how their mural came to be.

Meet the Author
Sarah Vázquez

One afternoon while in a public park, Sarah Vázquez and her son, Manuel, saw a wall covered with graffiti. They thought that the children who played in the park should have something better to look at. Ms. Vázquez wrote *The School Mural* to tell a story about what can happen when people decide to make things better for their community.

Meet the Illustrator
Melinda Levine

Melinda Levine lives in Oakland, California, with her husband, teenage daughter, gray silky cat, and big fluffy dog. She created the many-layered collages for *The School Mural* using cut paper, glue, scissors, and other paper-cutting tools.

Other books illustrated by Melinda Levine:

The Stone Soup Book of Friendship Stories
Water for One, Water for Everyone

Internet

Learn more about Sarah Vázquez and Melinda Levine, and about the ancient craft of paper cutting. Visit Education Place. **www.eduplace.com/kids**

Think About the Selection

1. Why do you think most of the children voted for Mei Lee's idea?

2. Why is a mural a good way to show school or community pride?

3. How do you think the adults felt about helping with the school mural?

4. If you could plan and paint a mural for your school, what would it show? Why?

5. **Connecting/Comparing** How might Tommy from *The Art Lesson* have helped make the mural?

Informing

Write Newspaper Headlines

A reporter wrote an article about the school mural. The headline said "Children Show School Pride." Think of other headlines the reporter could have used. Write headlines for his article.

Tips

- **Look at real newspaper headlines for ideas.**
- **Don't include words such as *the* and *a* in your headlines.**

Make Estimates

Find walls in your classroom or school which might be good places for a mural. Estimate the height and length of the walls. Record your estimates. Then use a yardstick to measure. Record the measurements.

Bonus List your measurements from longest to shortest.

Walls	Height	Length
classroom	10 ft.	12 ft.
hallway		

Give a Presentation

Look carefully at the mural in the story. Present it to a classmate or small group. Describe what is in the mural and explain why the students chose to include those scenes.

Internet

Take a Web Tour

Learn more about different types of art and the artists who make it. Visit Education Place and take a Web tour of an art museum.

www.eduplace.com/kids

SCHOOL COMICS

Check Your Progress

You read about some talented people in this theme. The talent show isn't over yet! You will be reading and comparing two more selections about talented people.

Tomie dePaola began this theme by saying that everyone has some kind of talent. Think about the selections in this theme. How did the characters discover their special talents?

Now you will read about people whose talents might surprise you. What would happen if these people did not try their best?

Read and Compare

Nonfiction

Zhang Jin and her friends have an amazing circus act!

Try these strategies:
Monitor and Clarify
Evaluate

Realistic Fiction

What happens when Raymond goes for his swimming test?

Try these strategies:
Compare and Contrast
Predict and Infer

Strategies in Action *Whenever you can, use all your reading strategies as you read the selections.*

Join the Circus!

by Zhang Jin as told to Mike McLeod
photographs by Ben Van Hook

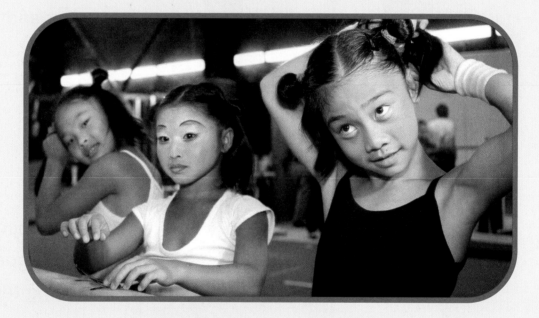

Hundreds of eyes are watching me as I stand motionless on a stage. A large, spool-like contraption whistles through the air high above my head. Tuning out the loud music, I focus on the sound behind me, slippered feet pattering toward my back. Then like a springing cat, my friend Wu Meng climbs up onto my shoulders — just in time to catch the spool about two inches in front of my nose!

Some kids wake up every day and go to school. I wake up and go to the circus. With my best friends Zhou Lu, Wu Meng, and Wang Wei Yi, all ten, I perform in an act called Diabolos for the Cirque du Soleil (SIRK due so-LAY) in Orlando, Florida.

Picture a spool-shaped, football-size toy balanced on a small cord. That's a diabolo. Then think of a performance that's a cross between juggling, gymnastics, and jumping rope. We fling our diabolos into the air like pancakes, doing somersaults and dances as we wait to catch them on our skinny ropes.

I've been practicing diabolos for four years — since I was eight and living near Beijing, China. In 1999, my friends and I were chosen to perform in the United States. Even though I was excited, I was a little afraid to leave my country and family behind. But Zhou Lu, Wu Meng, and Wang Wei Yi have become my new family.

We perform ten shows a week. To stay in shape, we jog first thing in the morning with our coach, Zhang Guije. Then we train for two hours. We practice spinning and catching the diabolos and tumbling. Sometimes we practice so much we callus our hands!

But when we're on the stage, we don't notice the calluses. As a hidden elevator platform lifts us to the stage, all we notice is each other. I know my friends so well that I can almost predict what they are going to do before they do it. I *have* to know what they're thinking when I've got all those diabolos flying toward my face.

You'd think I'd be exhausted, but I'm not. Performing with Cirque du Soleil *gives* me energy. And when I'm holding up the bottom of a pyramid, I need all the energy I can get!

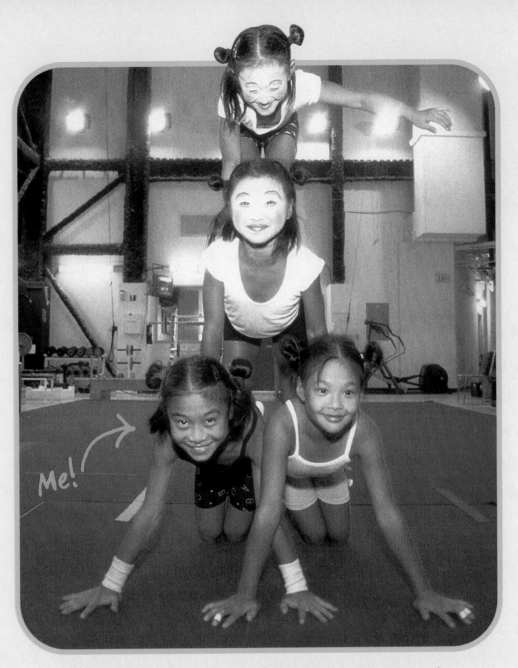

Me!

▲ Zhou Lu and I are on the bottom. Wu Meng is in the middle. Wang Wei Yi is at the top.

Cirque du Soleil isn't like any circus you've ever seen. There are no elephants, lion tamers, or trained seals.

Just what *will* you see at this weird and wild circus? Athletic "aerobats" scramble up a tower of wooden chairs. Acrobats twist in the air while hanging from long red scarves. Strongmen position themselves in human-size rings and spin around the stage.

Raymond's Best Summer

by Jean Rogers
illustrated by Jessie Reisch

Raymond and his friends on the Red Team are taking swimming lessons from a teacher named Lori. Raymond likes swimming, but there is one problem. He can only swim underwater, not on top of the water like everybody else. Now it's the last day of class, and Raymond is worried. What if he doesn't pass the swimming test?

• •

Friday morning Eloise and her mother came over early. "Boy," Eloise said as they got into the car, "I can't wait to get my certificate, can you?"

She looked at Raymond, but he didn't say anything. For the rest of the ride he was so busy worrying, he didn't answer any of Eloise's questions or pay any attention to her talk about the next set of swimming lessons they would be able to take the last two weeks of August.

She prattled away about the vacation her family was taking in July, but Raymond wasn't listening. What if he was one of the ones who would have to take the beginning lessons all over again? The rest of the Red Team would go right on without him and become intermediate swimmers and then swimmers. Why, they would become lifeguards and maybe even racers, and there he'd be, still down there on the bottom of the pool, thrashing around from side to side, getting nowhere.

Glumly he got into his swim trunks and sat beside Benjamin with the others, waiting for Red Team's turn to go through its paces.

By the time it was Red Team's turn, Raymond was completely downcast. The other team members were enthusiastically showing all the steps they had gone through in the process of learning to swim to earn their certificates. Although Raymond joined in everything, his heart wasn't in it.

When the time came to jump in and swim across the pool and back, the final test, Raymond was not surprised when Lori held him back and whispered to him to go sit down a second. He slumped down on the bench, wishing he could suddenly become invisible. This was even worse than he had imagined.

He couldn't bear to watch the others jump in and splash their way across the pool. He looked studiously at his feet, carefully watching trickles of water merge into little pools around his toes. He wished he had never signed up for lessons in the first place. You could probably go all through life without swimming anyway.

Lori told the Red Team members to sit down and put their towels around their shoulders. "Red Team has something to show you this morning," she said after she had blown her whistle for everyone to be quiet. "We have a very special swimmer on our team. Raymond, will you come up now?"

Raymond couldn't believe his ears, but he got up and stood beside Lori. "Raymond has learned to swim in his own way. He may be a porpoise in disguise, he swims underwater so well." She turned to Raymond as everyone, especially the rest of Red Team, laughed delightedly. "You won't mind giving us a demonstration of your underwater ability, will you, Raymond?"

Raymond was speechless, but he looked up at Lori and nodded.

"Okay, folks, here's Red Team's own porpoise. Go for it, Raymond."

With the sound of clapping loud in his ears, Raymond jumped into the water and took off. When he felt the other wall of the pool, he was so full of joy and excitement, he just turned and swam right back to the other side. He felt he could hold his breath forever if needed. He pushed up to find Lori's anxious face looking down at him.

"Why, Raymond!" she cried, helping him out of the pool. "How about that?" she said, turning to the audience. "This is the first time Raymond has ever done both laps! Even I didn't know he could do that."

"Am I going to get my certificate after all?" Raymond asked her as applause rang out.

"Why, Raymond, of course. Of course you'll get your certificate. Did you think you wouldn't?" She gave him a quick hug as she put his towel around his shoulders.

"Everyone on my team always passes." She grinned at him as he sat down. "Red Team is one hundred percent all the way. When the next class comes around, you'll find swimming will come naturally to you. Just relax and enjoy the water, Raymond. You've got the makings of a great swimmer."

Think and Compare

1. Both Raymond and Zhang Jin try their best. Compare how they feel when the time comes to perform.

2. Why is teamwork important in both *Join the Circus!* and *The School Mural*?

3. What would happen if the talented characters in this theme didn't practice? Give some examples.

4. Think about characters in this theme. Which character is most like you? Explain.

Strategies in Action How did using the reading strategies help you read better during this theme?

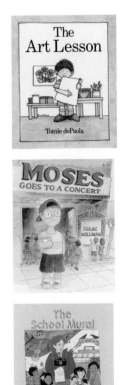

Explaining

Write an Interview

Choose a character from this theme that you want to interview. Write three questions you would ask that character. Then write the answers you might get from the character.

Tips

- **Get ideas for your questions from events in the story.**
- **Answer the questions as though the character is talking.**

Writing a Personal Narrative

A test may ask you to write about something that really happened to you. Read this sample test item for *Talent Show.* Then use the steps to help you write your answer.

> **Write about a time when you used a talent that you have.**

① Understand the prompt.

Find the key words in the prompt. Use them to understand what you need to do. Choose one experience to write about.

② Explore and plan.

Think about what happened. Use a chart to list the events and details in the order they happened.

Here is a sample planning chart.

I will write about a summer swim meet.	
What happened: I swam in a meet.	
Race 1: I won the race. Race 2: I came in last.	Detail: Three boys swam too. Detail: I had trouble at the end.

Write your paper.

First, draft your paper. Follow the chart you made.
Next, revise your paper. Look for places to add details.
Last, proofread your paper to correct errors.

Here is the beginning of a good personal narrative.

> Last Saturday I swam in the best swim meet
> I've had. I practiced for a week. Mom and Dad
> went with me. I swam three times in the meet.
> My first race was hard. Three boys
> swam, too. I was so excited! I won
> first place. I came in last in the
> second race because I was tired at
> the end. But it did not matter
> because I tried my best. I can't
> wait to swim in the next meet.

This glossary can help you find the meanings of some of the words in this book. The meanings given are the meanings of the words as they are used in the book. Sometimes a second meaning is also given.

A

accept

To say yes to: *I **accept** your offer of a new puppy.*

accident

Something you did not want or expect to happen: *Harry had an **accident** on his bicycle and fell down.*

advantage

Anything that is a help in getting what someone or something wants: *Frogs have the **advantage** of long, sticky tongues to catch fast flying insects.*

angry

Unhappy with someone; mad: *Tyler got **angry** when his sister dropped his glass.*

antennae

A pair of thin organs on the head of insects that can be used to touch and smell: *An ant's **antennae** can help it find food.*

antennae

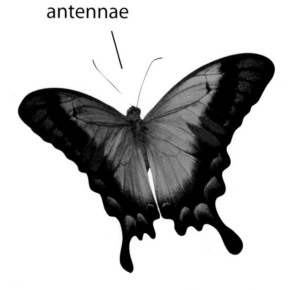

argument

A talk between people who do not agree and are mad at each other: *Miko had an **argument** with Leah over whose painting was better.*

attention

The act of looking and listening with care: *We paid close **attention** to the teacher as she read the story.*

audience

The people who gather to hear or see something: *A large **audience** sat in the theater waiting to see the movie.*

B

bakery

A place where foods such as bread and cake are made or sold: *The new **bakery** makes the best doughnuts.*

bakery

bolt

A flash of lightning: *The **bolt** of lightning was so bright it lit up my bedroom.*

C

chalk

A writing tool made mostly from seashells and used to write on blackboards or other surfaces: *Keisha used green **chalk** to draw pictures on the board.*

chalk

cocoon

Silky covering made by some insects to protect themselves until fully grown: *The caterpillars curled up in their **cocoons** and waited to grow.*

cocoon

colony

A group of animals, plants, or people living or growing together: *Ants live together in large **colonies**.*

command

An order: *I taught our dog the **commands**, "sit" and "speak."*

copy

To make another of something: *Everyone had to **copy** the letters of the alphabet from the board.*

crayon

A stick of colored wax used for drawing or writing: *Each box had eight **crayons** in it.*

crayons

culture

The things that a group of people do and think and the laws that the group lives by: *Sports like baseball are a part of our **culture**.*

customer

Person who often buys goods or services: *Ms. Ames is one of the **customers** who come into the coffee shop every morning.*

D

deaf

Unable to hear: *Mrs. Li watches your lips when you speak to her because she is **deaf**.*

distract

To make someone less interested in one thing and more interested in another: *My mother has to **distract** me from looking at the needle when I get my flu shot.*

dough

A thick mixture of flour and liquid that is used to make bread and other baked foods: *We cut the cookie **dough** into animal shapes.*

dough

E

event

Something that happens: *The first **event** of the party was a game of tag.*

F

fungus

A group of living things that are not plants or animals and have no flowers, leaves, or green coloring: *A mushroom is a type of fungus.*

fungus

fuss

To complain needlessly: *My aunt used to fuss about getting dirt on the porch.*

fussed

Form of **fuss**: *Jorge fussed about not getting any ice cream.*

G

groan

To make a deep sound low in the throat to show pain or anger: *I groan when I have an earache.*

groaned

Form of **groan**: *Kai groaned when the dentist told her she had a cavity.*

grumble

To say things in an unhappy tone: *We heard our dad grumble when he found the broken lamp.*

grumbled

Form of **grumble**: *Jenny grumbled when she was sent to bed early.*

grumpily

Acting in a cranky or upset way: *Andre grumpily got out of the pool when his mother called him to go to bed.*

guard

Watch over and keep safe: *My sister likes to eat my cookies, so I **guard** them when she's around.*

guarded

Form of **guard**: *The dog **guarded** the front door so no one could get past it.*

H

hearing

The sense by which sound is picked up; ability to hear: *My dog's sense of **hearing** is very good.*

horizon

The line along which the earth and the sky appear to meet: *Before night fell, the sun sat like a big orange ball on the **horizon**.*

I

ingredient

Part that makes up a mixture: *We bought all the **ingredients** we needed to make pumpkin pie.*

instrument

Thing that is used in making music: *Flutes are **instruments** that make high and soft sounds.*

L

larvae

Newly hatched insects that have no wings and look like worms: *Caterpillars are **larvae** that grow into butterflies and moths.*

larva

lightning

The flash of light in the sky in the middle of a storm: *The bright* **lightning** *lit up the sky.*

lightning

M

mural

A painting that is done on a wall or a ceiling: *The* **mural** *on the classroom wall was drawn by the students.*

N

newborn

Just brought into life: *My* **newborn** *baby brother hasn't left the hospital yet.*

O

officer

A member of a police force: *The* **officer** *made sure everyone at the parade was safe.*

officer

P

penalty

A punishment for breaking a rule or losing a game or sport: *The **penalty** for breaking the fire drill rules is no after-school sports.*

percussion

Musical instruments that create a special sound when struck: *Drums are **percussion** instruments.*

percussion

pest

A person or thing that is not nice to be around: *That fly is a **pest** because it keeps buzzing around my head.*

powder

Very small pieces of something: *That clown's face is covered with many different colored **powders**.*

practice

To do something over and over in order to be good at it: *Lelia and Rashawn **practice** jumping rope every day.*

pride

A feeling of happiness about something you or someone close to you has done: *Gino's parents were full of **pride** because he had learned to read so quickly.*

project

A special study or experiment done by students: *The class made a model of a volcano for their science **project**.*

promise

Say that you will do something: *I **promise** that I will always pick up my room.*

promised

Form of **promise**: *We* ***promised*** *to wash the car next Saturday.*

Q

quarrel

A talk between people who cannot agree and are mad at each other: *Marta and Joe had a* ***quarrel*** *about cleaning up after dinner.*

R

recipe

A set of directions for making something, usually food: *Gia wrote the* ***recipe*** *for oatmeal cookies on the board.*

GORP

(1 Batch)
2 cups raisins
3 cups peanuts
2 cups dried apricots
4 cups rice cereal
1 cup coconut
2 cups chocolate or carob chips

Mix all ingredients. Store in airtight container.

recipe

ruin

To harm something so that it cannot be fixed: *Grape juice can* ***ruin*** *a white shirt.*

rumble

Make a deep rolling sound: *We listen to the train* ***rumble*** *by our house every night.*

rumbled

Form of **rumble**: *The big truck* ***rumbled*** *down the highway.*

S

safety

Freedom from danger or harm: *We follow school* ***safety*** *rules so that no one gets hurt.*

scene

Place, picture, or drawing of a place or thing as seen by a viewer: *The postcards from Grandpa have* ***scenes*** *from Italy on them.*

sign

Use hand motions to express thoughts: *I will **sign** the news to the children, since they can't hear it for themselves.*

signs

Form of **sign**: *Sam **signs** with his hands to tell stories to children who can't hear.*

sketch

A picture drawn with lines but not colored in: *My parents made many **sketches** of our house before it was built.*

smock

A long shirt or apron worn over clothes to keep them clean: *We used an old shirt as a **smock** when we painted.*

spread

To cover something with something else: *Shaily **spread** butter on her toast.*

T

teenage

Between the ages of thirteen and nineteen: *Since Mary started going to her new school, she has lots of **teenage** friends.*

thunder

The deep, loud noise that comes from the sky during a storm: *The **thunder** was so loud we couldn't hear each other.*

tunnel

Underground or underwater passageway: *Some animals dig **tunnels** underground.*

tunnel

twin

Two children born at one birth: *My cousins are **twins**, and they look exactly like each other.*

twins

V

vibration

Rapid movement back and forth or up and down: *The **vibration** of the table was caused by the earthquake.*

W

weather

The state of the atmosphere at a given time or place, including heat, cold, rain, and wind: *Since the **weather** was warm and sunny, we had a picnic in the park.*

Acknowledgments

Main Literature Selections

Ant, by Rebecca Stefoff. Text copyright © 1998 by Rebecca Stefoff. Reprinted by permission of Benchmark Books, Marshall Cavendish, New York.

The Art Lesson, by Tomie dePaola. Copyright © 1989 by Tomie dePaola. Reprinted by permission of G.P. Putnam's Sons, a division of Penguin Putnam Inc.

Brothers & Sisters, by Ellen B. Senisi. Copyright © 1993 by Ellen B. Senisi. Reprinted by permission of Scholastic Inc.

Carousel, by Pat Cummings. Copyright © 1994 by Pat Cummings. Reprinted with permission of Simon & Schuster Books for Young Readers, Simon & Schuster Children's Publishing Division. All rights reserved.

"A Curve in the River" from *More Stories Julian Tells,* by Ann Cameron. Copyright © 1986 by Ann Cameron. Used by permission of Alfred A. Knopf, an imprint of Random House Children's Books, a division of Random House, Inc., and the Ellen Levine Agency.

The Great Ball Game: A Muskogee Story, by Joseph Bruchac, illustrated by Susan L. Roth. Text copyright © 1994 by Joseph Bruchac. Illustrations copyright © 1994 by Susan L. Roth. Reprinted by permission of Dial Books for Young Readers, a division of Penguin Putnam Inc.

Jalapeño Bagels, text by Natasha Wing, illustrated by Robert Casilla. Text copyright © 1996 by Natasha Wing. Illustrations copyright © 1996 by Robert Casilla. Reprinted with permission of Simon & Schuster Books for Young Readers, Simon & Schuster Children's Publishing Division. All rights reserved.

"Join the Circus!," by Zhang Jin as told to Mike McLeod, from the March 2001 issue of *National Geographic World.* Copyright © 2001 by the National Geographic Society. Reprinted by permission of the National Geographic Society.

Selection from *Little Grunt and the Big Egg,* by Tomie dePaola. Copyright © 1990 by Tomie dePaola. All rights reserved. Reprinted by permission of Holiday House, Inc. and Whitebird, Inc.

Excerpt from *Mighty Dinosaurs: Young Discoveries,* written by Judith Simpson. Copyright © 1996 by Weldon Owen Pty Ltd. Reprinted by permission of Weldon Owen Pty Ltd.

Moses Goes to a Concert, by Isaac Millman. Copyright © 1998 by Isaac Millman. Reprinted by permission of Farrar, Straus and Giroux, LLC.

Officer Buckle and Gloria, by Peggy Rathmann. Text and illustrations copyright © 1995 by Peggy Rathmann. Reprinted by permission of G. P. Putnam's Sons, a division of Penguin Putnam Inc.

Selection from *Raymond's Best Summer,* by Jean Rogers. Text copyright © 1990 by Jean Rogers. Used by permission of HarperCollins Publishers.

The School Mural, by Sarah Vázquez, illustrated by Melinda Levine. Copyright © 1998 Steck-Vaughn Company. Reprinted by permission from Steck-Vaughn Company. All rights reserved.

"Slippery Siblings" from the March 2001 issue of *Jack and Jill* magazine. Copyright © 2001 by Children's Better Health Institute, Benjamin Franklin Literary and Medical Society, Inc., Indianapolis, Indiana. Used by permission.

Talent Show, by Tomie dePaola. Copyright © 2005 by Tomie dePaola. Published by arrangement with Whitebird Inc. All rights reserved.

Thunder Cake, by Patricia Polacco. Copyright © 1990 by Patricia Polacco. Reprinted by permission of Philomel Books, a division of Penguin Putnam, New York.

Focus Selections

The Cool Crazy Crickets, by David Elliott, illustrated by Paul Meisel. Text copyright © 2000 by David Elliott. Illustrations copyright © 2000 by Paul Meisel. Reproduced by permission of Candlewick Press Inc., Cambridge, MA.

Links and Theme Openers

"Bat Attitude," by Lynn O'Donnell from the October 1997 issue of *3 2 1 Contact* magazine. Copyright © 1997 by Children's Television Workshop. Reprinted by permission of the publisher.

Calvin and Hobbes comic, by Bill Watterson, reprinted in the School Comics Media Link. Calvin and Hobbes © Watterson. Reprinted with permission of Universal Press Syndicate. All rights reserved.

"Carousel Designed for Kids," by Kathy Kranking from the June 1998 issue of *Ranger Rick* magazine. Copyright © 1998 by the National Wildlife Federation. Reprinted by permission of the National Wildlife Federation.

"Do Not Enter" from *Oh Grow Up!*, by Florence Parry Heide and Roxanne Heide Pierce. Text copyright © 1996 by Florence Parry Heide and Roxanne Heide Pierce. Reprinted by permission of Orchard Books, New York.

"Go to a Concert" from *Kids Make Music!*, by Avery Hart and Paul Mantell. Copyright © 1993 by Avery Hart & Paul Mantell. Reprinted by permission of Williamson Publishing Company.

"I Did Not Eat Your Ice Cream" from *Something Big Has Been Here*, by Jack Prelutsky. Copyright © 1990 by Jack Prelutsky. Reprinted by permission of HarperCollins Publishers.

"Little sister" from *Something on My Mind*, by Nikki Grimes. Copyright © 1978 by Nikki Grimes. Reprinted by permission of Dial Books for Young Readers, a division of Penguin Putnam Inc., and Curtis Brown Ltd.

Peanuts comics reprinted in the School Comics Media Link are reprinted from *Nothing Echoes Like an Empty Mailbox*, by Charles M. Schulz. PEANUTS © United Feature Syndicate. Reprinted by permission of United Feature Syndicate.

"The Story of Owney" from *Postal Pack for Elementary School Students*, published by the National Postal Museum at the Smithsonian Institution. Reprinted by permission.

"Sun & Ice" reprinted from *Out of the Bag: The Paper Bag Players Book of Plays*, by The Paper Bag Player. Text © 1997 by The Paper Bag Players. Reprinted by permission of Hyperion Books for Children and the Paper Bag Players.

"Welcome to the Kitchen," from *Young Chef's Nutrition Guide and Cookbook* by Carolyn Moore, Ph.D. R.D., Mimi Kerr and Robert Shulman, PhD. Copyright © 1990 by Barron's Educational Series. Reprinted by permission of the Barron's Educational Series.

"What is a family?" from *Fathers, Mothers, Sisters, Brothers: A Collection of Family Poems*, by Mary Ann Hoberman. Copyright © 1991 by Mary Ann Hoberman. Reprinted by permission of Little, Brown and Company (Inc.) and the Gina Maccoby Literary Agency.

Credits

Photography

474 (l) © PhotoDisc/Getty Images. **475** Artville.
476 Artville. **477** Digital Vision/PictureQuest.
478 Corbis Royalty Free. **479** © PhotoDisc/
Getty Images. **481** Corbis Royalty Free. **482**
Donna Day/Stone/Getty Images.

Assignment Photography

16–7, 216-17, 294-7, 351, 389, 425 (r) HMCo./
Joel Benjamin. **53, 85 (r), 111, 183 (r), 253, 293,
381, 455** HMCo./Ken Karp. **133, 313, 471** ©
HMCo./Michael Indresano Photography

Illustration

12–15 Chris Lensch. **58–59** Carolyn Iverson.
84 Mike Reed. **86** William Brinkley & Associates.
86-87 Nancy Gibson-Nash. **127–130** (border)
Patrick Gnan. **134-5** Ed Martinez. **158** Pat
Cummings. **159** Annette Cable. **160-61** Dave
Klug. **184-45** Eric Brace. **186-67** Copyright ©
2001 by Raúl Colón. **192, 214** Tom Brenner. **214
(c), 252 (c), (b) 253 (t)** Eileen Gilbride. **219** Clive
Scruton. **260, 292, 293** Jason Farris. **301,
303–306** Gail Piazza. **314-5** Paul Meisel. **346–8**
Tomie dePaola. **379, 380 (c) (bl)** Daniel Del Valle.
390, 424 (b) 425 George Ulrich. **432 (inset)
433–52** Melinda Levine. **453, 454 (b) 455** Jim
Kelly. **465, 467, 468** Jessie Reisch.